Name:

GCSE

Essential Exam Practice

With Answers

Key Stage 4
GCSE Foundation

Ruso Bradley, June Hall and Mark Haslam

Brookworth Books

Introduction

Mathematics is a subject where practice is the key to exam success. There is no better way of boosting your grade than practising the type of questions that will come up in your exams. It is no secret that many questions come up year after year, which is why the *Essential Exam Practice* range concentrates on these extremely important questions. It is also true that you can't predict exactly what will be in your exams, but if you try all the questions in this book, you are unlikely to get any nasty surprises!

About this book

This book is aimed at candidates taking the Foundation tier in GCSE Mathematics, and is suitable for all examination boards.

The questions are split into four main sections:
- Number (N)
- Algebra (A)
- Shape, Space & Measures (S)
- Handling Data (H)

Within these sections, the questions are grouped by topic, so you can quickly find what you're looking for. Answers to all questions can be found at the back of the book, so you can check that you're on the right track.

Instructions

 You **may** use a calculator to answer any question with this symbol.

 You **must not** use a calculator to answer any question with this symbol.

To answer some of the questions in this book, you will need a ruler graduated in centimetres and millimetres, an angle measurer or protractor, a pair of compasses and a calculator. You may also find tracing paper helpful. There is a formulae sheet on the inside front cover of this book. Alternatively, you can download one from www.brookworth.co.uk.

Good luck in your exams!

Contents

Number

NUMBERS AS WORDS

N1 **(a)** Write these in figures:

    (i) eight thousand, one hundred and fifty-seven,

        Answer .... *(1 mark)*

    (ii) fourteen thousand six hundred and twenty.

        Answer .... *(1 mark)*

(b) Write the following numbers as words.

    (i) 13 607

    ....

    .... *(1 mark)*

    (ii) 280 301

    ....

    .... *(1 mark)*

ORDERING NUMBERS & PLACE VALUE

N2 Write these numbers in order of size. Start with the smallest number.

(a) 42, 32, 46, 23, 33, 9

....

    Answer .... *(1 mark)*

(b) 497, 479, 517, 515, 482, 59

....

    Answer .... *(1 mark)*

N3 Write down the value of the 2 in each of these numbers.

(a) 10 280

        Answer .... *(1 mark)*

(b) 312 500

        Answer .... *(1 mark)*

(c) 60.25

        Answer .... *(1 mark)*

N4 **(a)** What is the value of the 5 in 19 256?

Answer.. *(1 mark)*

(b) Janine has three numbered cards.

| 3 | 2 | 5 |

(i) Rearrange the cards to make the largest possible number.

(1 mark)

(ii) What is the smallest number Janine can make using all three cards?

(1 mark)

N5 Choose from these numbers:

6   25   19
49   15   24
33   7   27

Write down all the:

(a) even numbers,

Answer..*(2 marks)*

(b) square numbers,

Answer..*(2 marks)*

(c) prime numbers.

Answer..*(2 marks)*

Number

N6

```
┌─────────────────────────────┐
│   100        28             │
│ 2      8          75        │
│    10        46             │
└─────────────────────────────┘
```

Which of the numbers above is:

(a) an odd number?

Answer .... *(1 mark)*

(b) a cube number?

Answer .... *(1 mark)*

(c) a prime number?

Answer .... *(1 mark)*

NON-CALCULATOR CALCULATIONS

N7 Work these out without using your calculator.

(a) 238 + 94

Answer .... *(1 mark)*

(b) 706 – 235

Answer .... *(1 mark)*

N8 Work these out without using your calculator.

(a) 13 × 42

Answer .... *(2 marks)*

(b) $2345 \div 7$

Answer ....(2 marks)

N9   Anil has 28 boxes of pens.
There are 24 pens in each box.
How many pens are there altogether?

Answer .... pens *(3 marks)*

N10 There were 713 runners in a half-marathon race.
The organisers of the race had to hire one safety marshal for every 23 runners.
How many safety marshals did they have to hire?

Answer .... safety marshals *(3 marks)*

Number

MULTIPLES & FACTORS

N11 Look at this list of numbers:

$$1, 3, 9, 12, 16$$

(a) From the list, write down all the multiples of 3.

Answer .... *(1 mark)*

(b) Write down all the numbers in the list that are factors of 12.

Answer .... *(1 mark)*

N12 From the list of numbers 2, 4, 6, 9, 10, 11, write down:

(a) all the multiples of 2,

Answer .... *(1 mark)*

(b) all the factors of 10.

Answer .... *(1 mark)*

N13 Look at this list of numbers: 1, 3, 10, 17, 30

(a) From the list, write down all the multiples of 5.

Answer .... *(1 mark)*

(b) Write down all the numbers in the list that are factors of 15.

Answer .... *(1 mark)*

N14 From the list of numbers 3, 5, 6, 14, 31, 42, write down:

(a) all the multiples of 7,

Answer .... *(1 mark)*

(b) all the factors of 18.

Answer .... *(1 mark)*

LCM & HCF

N15 Find the least common multiple of each pair of numbers.

(a) 4, 6

....

....

Answer .... *(3 marks)*

(b) 6, 15

....

....

Answer .... *(3 marks)*

N16 Find the highest common factor of each pair of numbers.

   (a) 15, 27

   ....

   ....

   Answer ....*(3 marks)*

   (b) 26, 39

   ....

   ....

   Answer ....*(3 marks)*

N17 What is the least common multiple of 12, 16 and 24?

   ....

   ....

   ....

   Answer ....*(4 marks)*

N18 What is the highest common factor of 12, 36 and 42?

   ....

   ....

   ....

   Answer ....*(4 marks)*

N19 Which two of these fractions are equivalent to $\frac{2}{9}$?

   $\frac{4}{12}$ $\frac{4}{18}$ $\frac{16}{63}$ $\frac{18}{81}$

   Answer ....*(2 marks)*

N20 Which of these fractions are equivalent to $\frac{6}{7}$?

   $\frac{16}{17}$ $\frac{12}{14}$ $\frac{18}{28}$ $\frac{66}{77}$ $\frac{30}{35}$

   Answer ....*(3 marks)*

Number

N21 (a) Work out:

    (i) $\frac{1}{3} + \frac{1}{6}$

Answer..*(2 marks)*

    (ii) $\frac{3}{4} - \frac{1}{2}$

Answer..*(2 marks)*

(b) There are 24 chocolates in a box.

$\frac{1}{4}$ of the chocolates are plain, the rest are milk chocolates.

How many milk chocolates are there?

....

....

....

Answer.. *(3 marks)*

N22 (a) Calculate:

    (i) $\frac{6}{7} \div 3$

Answer..*(2 marks)*

    (ii) $\frac{3}{4} \times \frac{1}{6}$

Answer..*(2 marks)*

(b) There are 36 houses in a street.

$\frac{1}{3}$ of the houses have red doors.

How many houses in the street DO NOT have red doors?

....

....

....

Answer..*(3 marks)*

N23 Arrange this set of fractions in order of size, smallest first.

$\frac{2}{3}$ $\frac{1}{4}$ $\frac{3}{7}$ $\frac{2}{5}$

Answer ....*(2 marks)*

N24 Arrange this set of fractions in order of size, largest first.

$\frac{1}{3}$ $\frac{1}{2}$ $\frac{2}{7}$ $\frac{5}{11}$

Answer ....*(2 marks)*

N25 A golf club has 360 members, 24 of whom are junior members. What fraction of members are juniors? Reduce your answer to its lowest terms.

Answer ....*(2 marks)*

N26 During November it snowed on five days. On what fraction of days in November did snow fall? Reduce your answer to its lowest terms.

Answer ....*(2 marks)*

N27 Find as a fraction in its lowest terms:

(a) $\frac{1}{7} + \frac{2}{35}$

Answer ....*(2 marks)*

(b) $\frac{4}{5} - \frac{1}{2}$

Answer ....*(2 marks)*

(c) $\frac{2}{10} \div \frac{1}{5}$

Answer ....*(2 marks)*

Number

FRACTIONS

N28 Find as a fraction in its lowest terms:

(a) $\frac{1}{20} + \frac{3}{4}$

Answer...(2 marks)

(b) $\frac{7}{8} - \frac{1}{4}$

Answer...(2 marks)

(c) $\frac{3}{11} \times \frac{22}{45}$

Answer...(2 marks)

N29 A bag holds 1 kg of salt. What fraction of its weight remains after 200 g of salt is used?

Answer...(2 marks)

DECIMALS

N30 (a) Write $\frac{3}{5}$ as a decimal.

....

Answer... (1 mark)

(b) (i) Write down the value of 0.25×100.

Answer... (1 mark)

(ii) Write down the value of $0.25 \div 100$.

Answer... (1 mark)

N31 Change 0.15 into a fraction in its lowest terms.

Answer...(2 marks)

N32 Without using a calculator, find:

(a) 5.26 + 3.83

Answer .... *(2 marks)*

(b) 18.3 − 4.7

Answer .... *(2 marks)*

(c) 4.7 × 5

Answer .... *(2 marks)*

(d) 23.6 ÷ 5

Answer .... *(2 marks)*

N33 A piece of elastic, 12.5 m long, is cut into 50 pieces of equal length.
How long is each piece?

....

Answer .... m *(1 mark)*

N34 7 people each have 1.3 kg of flour. How much flour do they have in total?

....

Answer .... kg *(1 mark)*

Number

PERCENTAGES

 N35 Order these fractions, decimals and percentages, smallest first.

$\frac{4}{5}$ 0.7 $\frac{3}{4}$ 85%

Answer ....(2 marks)

N36 Work out:

(a) 60% of 20

....

Answer ....(2 marks)

(b) 20% of 400

....

Answer ....(2 marks)

N37 Work out:

(a) 7% of 250

....

Answer ....(2 marks)

(b) 98% of 7000

....

Answer ....(2 marks)

N38 (a) Express 70% as a decimal.

....

Answer .... (1 mark)

(b) Express 12% as a fraction in its lowest terms.

Answer .... (1 mark)

(c) In a test, Carmen scored 28 out of 40. What percentage did she get?

Answer .... % (2 marks)

N39 Out of 32 teams in a basketball tournament, 20 of them play in red shorts.

    (a) What percentage of teams play in red shorts?

Answer .... % *(2 marks)*

    (b) What percentage of teams do not play in red shorts?

Answer ....% *(1 mark)*

N40 At a timber merchants, pine costs £20 per cubic foot.
Oak costs 15% more per cubic foot than pine.

    (a) How much, per cubic foot, does oak cost?

Answer £ ....*(3 marks)*

Mahogany costs 25% more than oak.

    (b) How much, per cubic foot, is mahogany?

Answer £ ....*(3 marks)*

N41 A new car is on sale for £12 000. The car's value will decrease by 15% each year.

    (a) How much will the car be worth after 1 year?

Answer £ ....*(3 marks)*

    (b) How much will the car be worth after 2 years?

Answer £ ....*(3 marks)*

Number

PERCENTAGES

N42 A double glazing manufacturer reduced the price of their most expensive front door from £620 to £540. What was the percentage reduction in price? Give your answer to 1 d.p.

....

....

....

Answer .... % *(3 marks)*

N43 Shortly after 25 December, the price of tinsel dropped from £2.10 to £1.60. What was the percentage reduction in price? Give your answer to 1 d.p.

....

....

....

Answer .... % *(3 marks)*

RATIO & PROPORTION

N44 Write the ratio 42 : 6 in its simplest form.

....

Answer .... *(1 mark)*

N45 Write the ratio 10 : 15 : 35 in its simplest form.

....

Answer .... *(1 mark)*

N46 Anthony and Sarah share £55 in the ratio 4 : 7. What is Sarah's share?

....

....

....

Answer £ .... *(2 marks)*

N47 John, Tariq and Beth share £45 in the ratio 2 : 3 : 4. What is John's share?

....

....

....

Answer £ .... *(3 marks)*

N48 2 kg of tuna costs £2.96.
How much will 5 kg cost?

....

....

Answer £ .... *(2 marks)*

N49 4 pints of orange juice cost £3.12.
How much will 11 pints of orange juice cost?

....

....

Answer £ .... *(2 marks)*

N50 A chocolate cake for 5 people requires 75 g of sugar.
Daphne makes a chocolate cake for 8 people.
Calculate the weight of sugar that Daphne needs.

....

....

Answer .... g *(2 marks)*

N51 A pizza for 7 people requires 840 g of flour. Winston makes a pizza for 4 people.
Calculate the weight of flour that Winston needs for his pizza.

....

....

Answer .... g *(2 marks)*

N52 A sports shop is selling second-hand golf balls for 75p each.

(a) Jerry buys 20 golf balls.
How much change does she get from £20?

....

....

Answer £ .... *(2 marks)*

(b) How many golf balls could she buy for £20?

....

....

Answer .... golf balls *(2 marks)*

Number

N53 Kevin earns £411.60 per week.
He works 8 hours a day and 5 days a week.

    (a) How much is Kevin paid for one day's work?

....

Answer £.. *(1 mark)*

    (b) What is Kevin's hourly rate of pay?

....

Answer £.. *(1 mark)*

N54 Saeed had his gas meter read on 5 June. The reading was 12 692.
On 7 August another reading was taken as 14 124.

    (a) How many units had Saeed used between 5 June and 7 August?

....

Answer.. *(1 mark)*

    (b) A unit of gas costs 7.5p.
How much will Saeed have to pay for his gas?

....

....

Answer £.. *(2 marks)*

N55

      40 Envelopes   120 Envelopes

        £1.90   £7.60

David wants to buy 240 envelopes.

    (a) How many packs of 40 envelopes would he need?

....

Answer.. *(1 mark)*

    (b) What is the cheapest way of buying 240 envelopes?

....

....

....

Answer.. *(3 marks)*

Number

N56 Two different-sized packs of cereal are shown.

Which pack is better value for money?
Show clearly how you decide.

....

....

....

....

Answer..*(4 marks)*

POWERS & ROOTS

N57 Without using your calculator, work out:

(a) 5^3

....

Answer.. *(1 mark)*

(b) 3^4

....

Answer.. *(1 mark)*

(c) $\sqrt{36}$

Answer.. *(1 mark)*

N58 Work out the value of:

(a) 1.4^3

Answer.. *(1 mark)*

(b) $\sqrt{34.81}$

Answer.. *(1 mark)*

19

Number

POWERS & ROOTS

N59 Write as a power of 9:

(a) $9^2 \times 9^3$

....

Answer... *(1 mark)*

(b) $9^4 \div 9^2$

....

Answer... *(1 mark)*

N60 A square-shaped patio has an area of 12.25 m².
What is the length of one side of the patio?

....

....

Answer...m *(2 marks)*

N61 A cube shaped box of sugar has a volume of 274.625 cm³.
What is the length of one side of the box?

....

....

Answer...cm *(2 marks)*

PRIME FACTORISATION

N62 The prime factorisation of a certain number is

$$2^2 \times 3^2 \times 7$$

(a)   What is the number?

Answer... *(1 mark)*

(b)   Write down the prime factorisation of 90.

....

....

....

Answer...*(2 marks)*

N63 Write 275 as a product of its prime factors using index notation.

....

....

....

Answer...*(2 marks)*

Number

STANDARD INDEX FORM

N64 (a) Write 920 000 in standard form.

....

Answer .... *(1 mark)*

(b) Write 4.3×10^4 as an ordinary number.

....

Answer .... *(1 mark)*

N65 (a) What is 0.0423 in standard form?

....

Answer .... *(1 mark)*

(b) What is 5.9×10^7 written as an ordinary number?

....

Answer .... *(1 mark)*

N66 The population of Indonesia is roughly 230 million.
Write the population of Indonesia in standard form.

....

Answer .... *(1 mark)*

N67 The Moon is 384 000 km from the Earth's surface.
Write the distance between the Moon and the Earth in standard form.

....

Answer ....km *(1 mark)*

ROUNDING & ESTIMATING

N68 (a) Round these to the nearest whole number.

(i) 6.72

Answer .... *(1 mark)*

(ii) 14.09

Answer .... *(1 mark)*

(b) Write these numbers correct to the nearest 10.

(i) 182.5

Answer .... *(1 mark)*

(ii) 8576

Answer .... *(1 mark)*

Number

N69 **(a)** Write these numbers correct to the nearest 100.

    (i) 10 214

                      Answer.. *(1 mark)*

    (ii) 3425.6

                      Answer.. *(1 mark)*

(b) Write these numbers correct to the nearest 1000.

    (i) 13 720

                      Answer.. *(1 mark)*

    (ii) 2545.7

                      Answer.. *(1 mark)*

N70 Convert the improper fraction $\frac{8}{7}$ to a decimal correct to:

(a) 2 decimal places,

                      Answer.. *(1 mark)*

(b) 2 significant figures.

                      Answer.. *(1 mark)*

N71 Estimate the answer to this: $\dfrac{79.6 + 21.8}{32.3 - 9.9}$

                      Answer...*(2 marks)*

N72 Estimate the answer to this: $\dfrac{41.2 \times 11.3}{19.6 + 21.7}$

                      Answer...*(2 marks)*

N73 Use your calculator to work this out:

$$\frac{29.42 \times 0.0941}{15.2 \times 8.42}$$

(a) Write down your full calculator display.

Answer.. *(1 mark)*

(b) Round your answer to 2 significant figures.

Answer.. *(1 mark)*

N74 Use your calculator to work this out:

$$\frac{9.59 + 0.024}{7.2 - 1.4}$$

(a) Write down your full calculator display.

Answer.. *(1 mark)*

(b) Round your answer to 1 significant figure.

Answer.. *(1 mark)*

N75 The diagram shows an aeroplane 126 m above the sea and a submarine below the surface.

Aeroplane   +126 m

Sea level   0 m

Sea bed   −132 m

(a) How far is the sea bed below the aeroplane?

....

Answer.. m *(1 mark)*

The base of the submarine is 46 m above the sea bed.

(b) How far below sea level is the base of the submarine?

....

Answer..m *(2 marks)*

Number

NEGATIVE NUMBERS

N76 **(a)** According to the map, how much warmer is Portugal than Sweden?

....

....

Answer ....°C *(1 mark)*

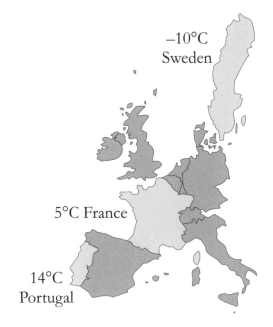

−10°C
Sweden

5°C France

14°C
Portugal

(b) The temperatures drop to 10°C below those shown on the map.
Work out the new temperatures in Sweden and France.

....

....

Sweden .... °C

France .... °C *(2 marks)*

N77 Write these numbers in order of size.
Start with the smallest number.

(a) 6   −4   3   −5   −8

....

Answer .... *(1 mark)*

(b) −1   1   3   −2   0

....

Answer .... *(1 mark)*

N78 Complete these calculations:

(a) −6 + −4 = ...   **(b)** −6 − −4 = ...

(c) 9 × −3 = ...   **(d)** 9 ÷ −3 = ... *(4 marks)*

N79 Complete these calculations:

(a) −3 + 5 = ...   **(b)** −3 − −5 = ...

(c) −12 × −3 = ...   **(d)** −12 ÷ −3 = ... *(4 marks)*

Algebra

A1 Madhur buys p potatoes.
Three of the potatoes are bad, so she throws them away.

(a) Write down an expression, in terms of p, for the number of potatoes Madhur has left.

Answer .... *(1 mark)*

Madhur has c carrots.
She buys four more.

(b) Write down an expression, in terms of c, for the number of carrots Madhur has now.

Answer .... *(1 mark)*

The carrots take m minutes to cook.
The potatoes take twice as long.

(c) Write down an expression, in terms of m, for how long the potatoes take to cook.

Answer .... minutes *(1 mark)*

A2 Simplify these expressions:

(a) $6a \times 2b$

....

Answer .... *(1 mark)*

(b) $7a^2 - 4a^2$

....

Answer .... *(1 mark)*

(c) $4a + 3b - 3a + b$

....

Answer ....*(2 marks)*

A3 Simplify the following:

(a) $4x + 5y - 3x + 6y$

....

Answer ....*(2 marks)*

(b) $a^2 \times a^4$

....

Answer .... *(1 mark)*

(c) $\dfrac{x^6}{x^4}$

....

Answer .... *(1 mark)*

Algebra

A4 Solve the following equations.

(a) $x - 4 = 7$

....

Answer $x = $.. *(1 mark)*

(b) $2x = 4$

....

Answer $x = $.. *(1 mark)*

(c) $\frac{x}{3} = 6$

....

Answer $x = $.. *(1 mark)*

A5 Find x:

(a) $x + 3 = 11$

....

Answer $x = $.. *(1 mark)*

(b) $3x = 21$

....

Answer $x = $.. *(1 mark)*

(c) $\frac{x}{2} = 8$

....

Answer $x = $.. *(1 mark)*

A6 Solve these equations.

(a) $2x = 10$

....

Answer $x = $.. *(1 mark)*

(b) $9x + 6 = 33$

....

....

Answer $x = $.. *(2 marks)*

(c) $3x - 4 = 8 - x$

....

....

....

Answer $x =$ ....*(3 marks)*

(d) $3(2x - 1) = 45$

....

....

....

Answer $x =$ ....*(3 marks)*

A7   Solve the equations:

(a) $5x = 2$

....

Answer $x =$ ....*(1 mark)*

(b) $15 - 3x = 3$

....

....

Answer $x =$ ....*(2 marks)*

(c) $16 - 2x = 4x + 10$

....

....

....

Answer $x =$ ....*(3 marks)*

(d) $4(2x - 1) = 7x + 11$

....

....

....

Answer $x =$ ....*(3 marks)*

Algebra

SUBSTITUTING INTO FORMULAE

A8   Jonti's recipe book gives the time needed to roast a joint of beef.

> 68 minutes per kilogram, plus 32 minutes

(a)   How long should it take to roast a 2.1 kg joint of beef?
Give your answer in hours and minutes, correct to the nearest minute.

....

....

....

Answer .... hours .... mins *(4 marks)*

(b)   Another joint of beef took 2 hours and 14 minutes to roast.
What was the weight of this joint?

....

....

....

Answer...kg *(3 marks)*

A9   Using the formula $a = 2b + 4$, find a when:

(a) $b = 5.9$

....

Answer $a =$...*(2 marks)*

(b) $b = 6.3$

....

Answer $a =$ ....*(2 marks)*

A10   Using the formula $p = 3q - 7$, find p when:

(a) $q = 4$

....

Answer $p =$ ....*(2 marks)*

(b) $q = 2$

....

Answer $p =$...*(2 marks)*

(c) $q = -10$

....

Answer $p =$ ....*(2 marks)*

A11 Use the formula $C = \frac{5}{9}(F - 32)$ to find C when:

(a) $F = 41$

....

....

Answer $C =$ .... *(2 marks)*

(b) $F = 86$

....

....

Answer $C =$ .... *(2 marks)*

(c) $F = 149$

....

....

Answer $C =$ .... *(2 marks)*

A12 Find the value of $A = p^2 + 3r$ when:

(a) $p = 3$ and $r = 6$

....

....

Answer $A =$ .... *(2 marks)*

(b) $p = 5$ and $r = 4$

....

....

Answer $A =$ .... *(2 marks)*

(c) $p = 10$ and $r = 7$

....

....

Answer $A =$ .... *(2 marks)*

Algebra

WRITING FORMULAE

A13 The time needed to cook a turkey is given as 20 minutes per pound plus an extra 20 minutes.

(a) Write down a formula for the time taken, T minutes, to cook a turkey of weight W lb.

....

....

Answer $T =$ ....*(2 marks)*

(b) How long will a turkey weighing 8 lb take to cook? Give your answer in hours.

....

....

Answer...hours *(2 marks)*

A14 Salespeople are paid according to how many hours they work and the number of products they sell.

(a) If a salesperson receives £6 per hour plus £2 for every item sold, write down a formula for their pay, £P, in terms of hours worked, H, and number of items sold, S.

....

....

Answer $P =$ ....*(2 marks)*

(b) How much does a salesperson get paid for 37 hours work if 95 items are sold?

....

....

Answer £...*(2 marks)*

REARRANGING FORMULAE

A15 (a) Make n the subject of the formula $m = 5n - 1$.

Answer $n =$ ....*(2 marks)*

(b) Make q the subject of the formula $p = q^2 + 2$.

Answer $q =$ ....*(2 marks)*

A16 You are given the formula $a = 2bc^2$.

(a) Rearrange the formula to give b in terms of a and c.

Answer $b =$..*(2 marks)*

(b) Rearrange the formula to give c in terms of a and b.

Answer $c =$..*(3 marks)*

A17 (a) Complete this table of values for $y = 2x + 2$.

x	-2	-1	0	1	2	3
$y = 2x + 2$			2			

(2 marks)

(b) Draw the graph of $y = 2x + 2$ on the grid below.

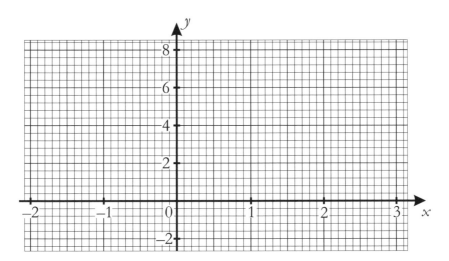

(2 marks)

(c) Use your graph to find:

(i) the value of x when $y = 7$,

Answer $x =$..*(1 mark)*

(ii) the value of y when $x = 1.5$.

Answer $y =$..*(1 mark)*

Algebra

STRAIGHT LINE GRAPHS

A18 **(a)** Complete the following table of values for the function $y = 2x - 2$.

x	-2	-1	0	1	2	3
$y = 2x - 2$				0		

(2 marks)

(b) Draw the graph of $y = 2x - 2$ on the grid below.

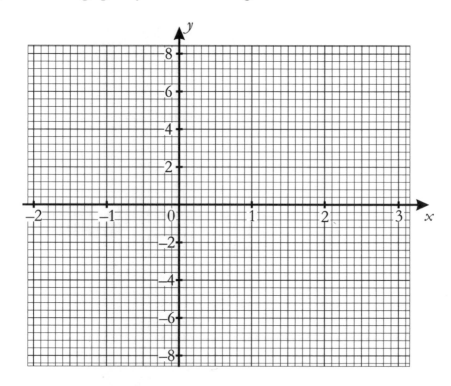

(2 marks)

(c) Using your graph:

(i) find the value of y when $x = -1.5$

Answer $y =$.. *(1 mark)*

(ii) solve $\quad 3 = 2x - 2$

Answer $x =$...*(2 marks)*

A19 Which of these lines is parallel to the line with equation $2y = 4x - 6$?

| $y = 3 - 2x$ | $y = 4x - 3$ | $y = 2x + 18$ |

....

....

Answer...*(2 marks)*

Algebra

A20 By first completing the tables of values, draw the graphs of:

(a) $y = 2x$

x	0	1	2	3
$y = 2x$	0			

(b) $y = 6 - x$

x	0	1	2	3
$y = 6 - x$	6			

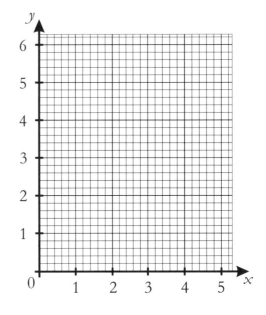

(6 marks)

(c) Write down the coordinates of the point where the graphs cross.

Answer (................................, ...) *(1 mark)*

A21 List all the possible values of x such that $-5 \leqslant x < 4$, where x is an integer.

Answer...*(2 marks)*

A22 Write down all the values of x that satisfy $-2 < x \leqslant 6$, where x is an integer.

Answer...*(2 marks)*

A23 (a) Represent $x < 4$ on the number line below.

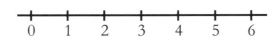

(1 mark)

(b) Represent $-1 < x \leqslant 3$ on the number line below.

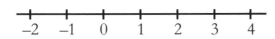

(2 marks)

33

Algebra

INEQUALITIES

A24 **(a)** Solve the inequality $4x + 3 < 5$.

....

....

....

Answer ....(2 marks)

(b) Solve the inequality $5(3x - 7) > 10$.

....

....

....

....

Answer ....(3 marks)

TRIAL & IMPROVEMENT

A25 Ross is using trial and improvement to find a solution to the equation $x^3 + x = 500$.
The table shows his first two trials.

x	$x^3 + x$	Comment
7	350	Too small
8	520	Too big

Continue the table to find a solution to the equation to 1 decimal place.

Answer $x =$ ....(3 marks)

A26 The equation

$$x^3 - 5x = 17$$

has a solution between 3 and 4.
Use trial and improvement to find this solution correct to 1 decimal place.

Answer $x =$...*(4 marks)*

A27 (a) Expand $\quad 7(a + 3)$

....

Answer.. *(1 mark)*

(b) Factorise $\quad 9b - 6$

....

Answer.. *(1 mark)*

A28 (a) Expand and simplify $\quad 3(2m + 5n) - 4n$

....

....

Answer...*(2 marks)*

(b) Factorise $\quad 5x^2 - 10x$

....

....

Answer...*(2 marks)*

Algebra

EXPANSION & FACTORISATION

A29 Expand the brackets and simplify $(x + 3)(x + 2)$

....

....

....

Answer..*(3 marks)*

A30 Expand the brackets and simplify $(3x - 2)(x + 1)$

....

....

....

Answer..*(3 marks)*

QUADRATIC GRAPHS

A31 **(a)**   Complete this table of values for $y = x^2 + 2$.

x	−2	−1	0	1	2
$y = x^2 + 2$		3			

(2 marks)

(b)   Draw the graph of $y = x^2 + 2$ on the grid below.

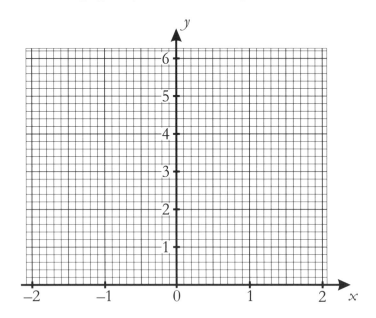

(2 marks)

(c)   Use your graph to find the value of y when $x = 1.4$.

Answer $y =$..*(1 mark)*

A32 (a) By first completing the table, draw the graph of $y = 3x^2$ for values of x from 0 to 3.

x				
x^2				
$y = 3x^2$				

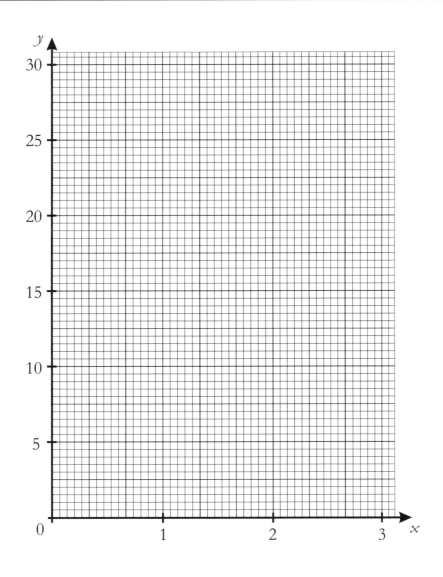

(4 marks)

(b) Use your graph to find a value of x when $y = 20$.

Answer $x =$ .... *(1 mark)*

Algebra

A33   The distance–time graph below shows Pippa's journey from her home to her local sports centre. On her way, she takes a parcel to the post office.

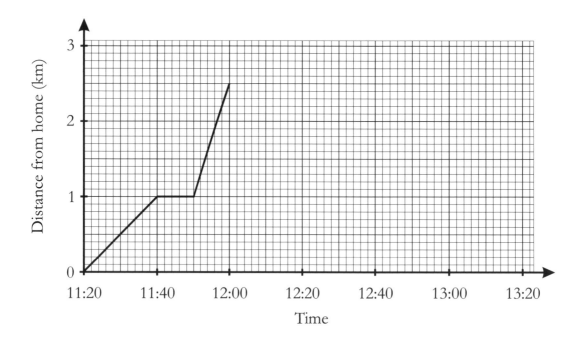

(a)   What time did Pippa set off?

Answer .... *(1 mark)*

(b)   How long was Pippa at the post office?

....

Answer ....minutes *(1 mark)*

(c)   What is the distance from Pippa's home to the sports centre?

Answer .... km *(1 mark)*

(d)   Pippa stays at the sports centre until 12:40.
She then travels home at a constant speed, arriving at 13:10.
Complete the travel graph.   *(2 marks)*

A34 The distance–time graph below shows Pete's cycle ride.
He starts and finishes at home.

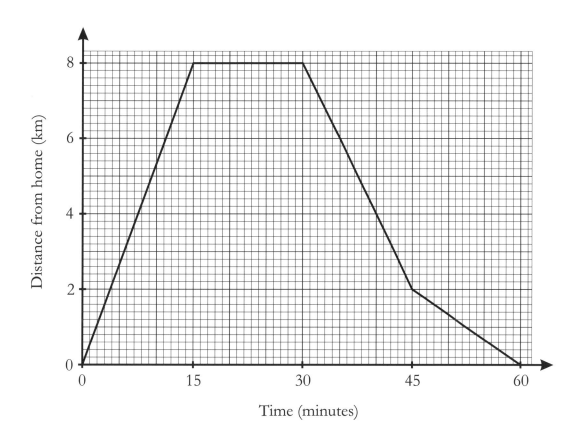

(a) How far did Pete cycle in total?

....

Answer .... km *(1 mark)*

(b) How far from home was Pete after 35 minutes?

Answer .... km *(1 mark)*

(c) How fast was Pete travelling after 25 minutes?

....

Answer .... km/minute *(1 mark)*

Algebra

CONVERSION GRAPHS

A35

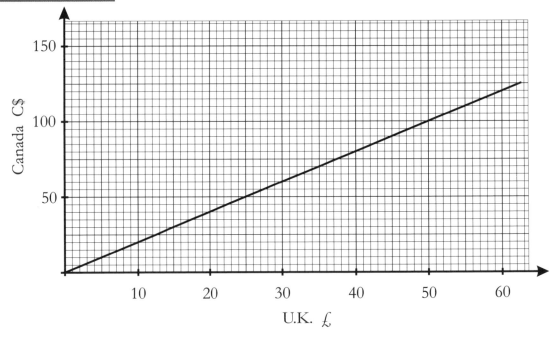

(a) Use the conversion graph to convert £20 into Canadian dollars.

Answer C$ .... *(1 mark)*

(b) What is C$100 in pounds sterling?

Answer £... *(1 mark)*

A36 This graph relates temperatures in degrees Fahrenheit (°F) to temperatures in degrees Celsius (°C).

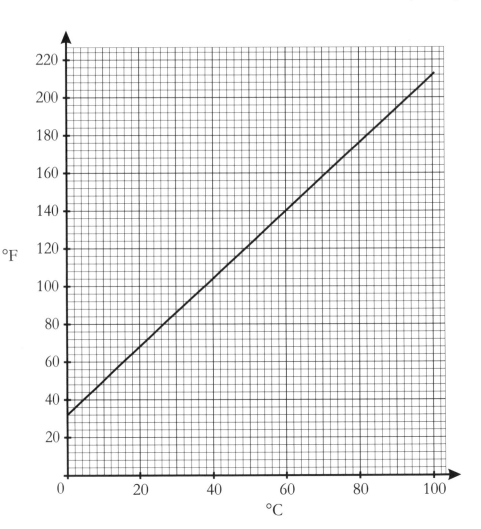

Algebra

CONVERSION GRAPHS

(a) Use the graph to convert 80°C to degrees Fahrenheit.

Answer .... °F *(1 mark)*

(b) What is 100°F in degrees Celsius?

Answer..°C *(1 mark)*

RECOGNISING GRAPHS

A37 Water is poured into these odd shaped vases at the same constant rate.
Match each vase to the correct graph.

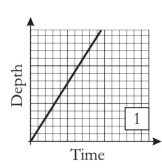

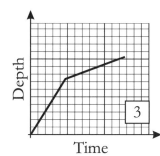

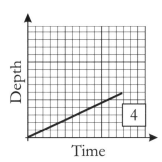

Vase *A* matches graph ....   Vase *B* matches graph ....

Vase *C* matches graph ....   Vase *D* matches graph ....

(3 marks)

Algebra

A38 Below are the first three patterns in a sequence.

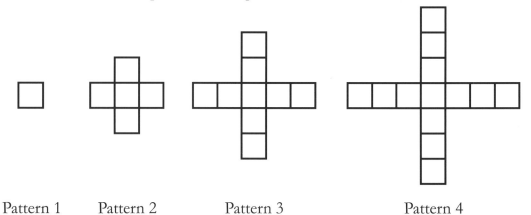

Pattern 1   Pattern 2   Pattern 3   Pattern 4

(a) Complete the following table.

Pattern	1	2	3	4
Number of Squares	1	5		

(1 mark)

(b) How many squares are there in Pattern 5?

Answer .... *(1 mark)*

(c) Here is a rule for working out the number of squares:

> Multiply the pattern number by 4 and subtract 3

How many squares are there in Pattern 10?

....

Answer .... *(1 mark)*

Algebra

A39 Below are the first three patterns in a sequence.

Pattern 1   Pattern 2   Pattern 3

(a) Complete the following table:

Pattern	1	2	3	4	5
Number of Squares	1	3			

(2 marks)

(b) Explain how you found the number of squares each time.

....

.... *(1 mark)*

(c) How many squares will be in pattern 9?

....

Answer.. *(1 mark)*

A40 Below are the first four terms of a number sequence.

5, 8, 11, 14, ...

(a) Write down the next two terms.

Answer ...., ...*(2 marks)*

(b) Describe how you worked out your answer to part **(a)**.

....

.... *(1 mark)*

(c) What is the 8th term in the sequence?

....

Answer.. *(1 mark)*

(d) Find the formula for the *n*th term of the sequence.

....

....

....

Answer..(2 marks)

43

Algebra

PATTERNS & SEQUENCES

A41 The following is a number pattern. One number is missing.

$$9, 11, 13, ..., 17$$

(a) Write down the missing number.

Answer .... *(1 mark)*

(b) Explain how you found the missing number.

....

.... *(1 mark)*

(c) What is the 6th term in the sequence?

....

Answer .... *(1 mark)*

(d) Work out a formula for the *n*th term in the sequence.

....

....

....

Answer ....*(2 marks)*

A42 Below are the first four terms of a number sequence.

$$1, 3, 6, 10, ...$$

(a) Write down the next two terms.

Answer ...., ...*(2 marks)*

(b) What are the numbers in this sequence called?

Answer .... *(1 mark)*

A43 Below are the first four terms of a number sequence.

$$1, 4, 9, 16, ...$$

(a) Write down the next two terms.

Answer ...., ...*(2 marks)*

(b) What are the numbers in this sequence called?

Answer .... *(1 mark)*

Shape, Space & Measures

S1 Write down the mathematical name for each of the following shapes.

(a)

Answer .... *(1 mark)*

(b)

Answer .... *(1 mark)*

(c)

Answer .... *(1 mark)*

S2 Write down the mathematical name for each of the following shapes.

(a)

Answer .... *(1 mark)*

(b)

Answer .... *(1 mark)*

(c)

Answer .... *(1 mark)*

Shape, Space & Measures

S3

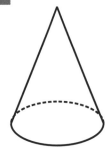

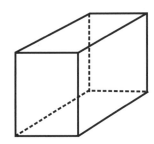

Shape A   Shape B

(a) Give the mathematical name for:

(i) shape A,

Answer .... *(1 mark)*

(ii) shape B.

Answer .... *(1 mark)*

(b) How many:

(i) edges does shape B have?

Answer .... *(1 mark)*

(ii) vertices does shape B have?

Answer .... *(1 mark)*

(iii) faces does shape B have?

Answer .... *(1 mark)*

S4

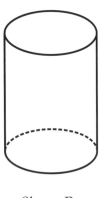

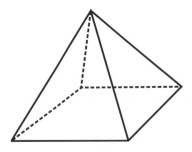

Shape P   Shape Q

(a) Give the mathematical name for:

(i) shape P,

Answer .... *(1 mark)*

(ii) shape Q.

Answer .... *(1 mark)*

(b) How many:

    (i) edges does shape Q have?

        Answer .... *(1 mark)*

    (ii) vertices does shape Q have?

        Answer .... *(1 mark)*

    (iii) faces does shape Q have?

        Answer .... *(1 mark)*

NETS, PLANS & ELEVATIONS

S5 Below is the net of a shape.

What is the mathematical name for the shape this net will make?

        Answer .... *(1 mark)*

S6 Below is the net of a shape.

What is the mathematical name for the shape this net will make?

        Answer .... *(1 mark)*

Shape, Space & Measures

S7

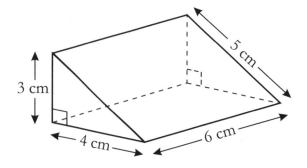

Not to scale

Draw a full-size net for the triangular prism above.

(4 marks)

S8 The drawing shows a cuboid with a triangular prism removed.
All measurements are in centimetres.

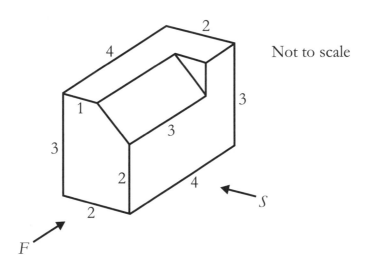

Not to scale

On the grids below, draw full size the front (*F*) and side (*S*) elevations.

Front elevation (*F*):

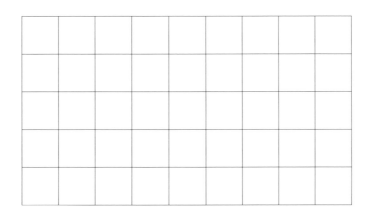

Side elevation (*S*):

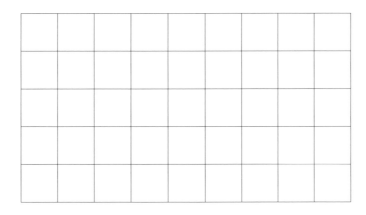

(4 marks)

Shape, Space & Measures

NETS, PLANS & ELEVATIONS

S9 Two 3-D shapes are combined to form a solid shape.
The plan, front and side elevations of the solid shape are shown below.

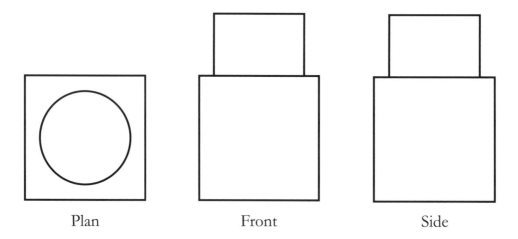

Plan   Front   Side

(a) Give the mathematical names of the two shapes used.

Answer .... and .... *(2 marks)*

(b) Sketch the shape.

(2 marks)

S10 Draw all the lines of symmetry on the following shapes.

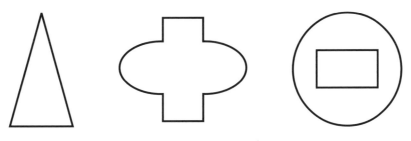

(3 marks)

S11 A design is made up of four congruent shapes, one of which is shown below.
Complete the design, so that the broken lines are lines of symmetry.

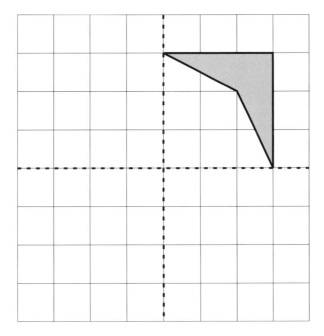

(3 marks)

S12 Next to each of the diagrams below, write down the order of rotational symmetry.

(a)

....

(b)

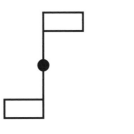

....

(c)

....

(d)

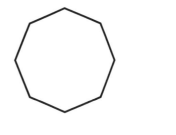

....

(4 marks)

51

Shape, Space & Measures

S13 **(a)** Which of these shapes has 3 lines of symmetry?

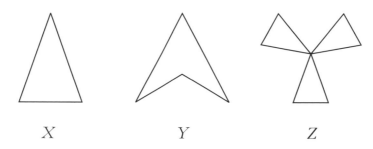

X   Y   Z

Answer... *(1 mark)*

(b) Draw another shape with 3 lines of symmetry.
Mark clearly on your drawing all 3 lines.

(2 marks)

READING SCALES

S14 **(a)** John is trying to measure the length of his eraser.

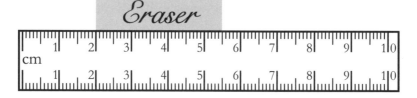

(i) How long is his eraser?

....

Answer..cm *(2 marks)*

(ii) Peter has an eraser that is 8.5 cm long.
Draw Peter's eraser below the ruler. *(1 mark)*

(b) Using your ruler, measure exactly the length of the line below.

Answer... cm *(1 mark)*

S15 **(a)** Here is the dial on a weighing machine.

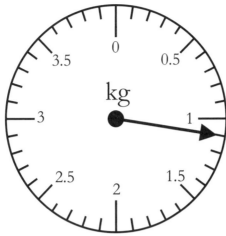

(i) Write down the weight that the dial is displaying.

Answer.. kg *(1 mark)*

(ii) On the dial, draw the new position of the pointer if a further 1.7 kg is added to the machine.

....*(2 marks)*

(b) Using your ruler, measure exactly the length of the line below.

Answer.. cm *(1 mark)*

S16 **(a)** What is 352 cm in metres?

....

Answer.. m *(1 mark)*

(b) What is 1.6 kg in grams?

....

Answer.. g *(1 mark)*

(c) 1 kg is approximately 2 lb.
What is 20 kg in pounds?

....

Answer.. lb *(1 mark)*

Shape, Space & Measures

METRIC & IMPERIAL UNITS

S17 **(a)** How many centimetres are there in 4.5 m?

....

Answer .... cm *(1 mark)*

(b) How many grams are there in 25 kg?

....

Answer .... g *(1 mark)*

(c) 1 litre is about 1.75 pints.
How many pints are there in 10 litres?

....

Answer .... pints *(1 mark)*

S18 **(a)** Which metric unit of length would you use to measure the length of a bus?

Answer .... *(1 mark)*

(b) Using the unit you gave in part **(a)** estimate the length of a bus.

Answer .... *(1 mark)*

(c) Using a suitable metric unit of weight, estimate the weight of a loaf of bread.

Answer .... *(2 marks)*

(d) Using a suitable imperial unit of weight, estimate the weight of an apple.

Answer .... *(2 marks)*

(e) Using a suitable metric unit of capacity, estimate the amount of water in a full bucket.

Answer .... *(2 marks)*

(f) Using a suitable imperial unit of capacity, estimate the amount of cola in a full can.

Answer .... *(2 marks)*

S19 Given that 5 miles is approximately 8 km, how many miles is 25 km?

....

....

Answer .... *(2 marks)*

S20 Given that 4 litres is about 7 pints, how many litres are there in 10 pints?
Give your answer to 1 d.p.

....

....

Answer .... *(2 marks)*

Shape, Space & Measures

S21 Below is a bus timetable for the journey from Oxford to Southampton.

Oxford	10:15
Abingdon	10:35
Newbury	11:15
Basingstoke	11:40
Winchester	12:30
Southampton	13:15

(a) At what time does the bus leave Newbury?

Answer .... *(1 mark)*

(b) How long does the bus take to travel between Basingstoke and Southampton?
Give your answer in hours and minutes.

....

Answer ....*(2 marks)*

S22 Kerry is travelling through Sweden. She wants to take a train from Göteborg to Malmö.
Below is the train timetable.

Göteborg	10:42	12:42	14:42
Halmstad	12:03	14:03	16:03
Helsingborg	12:59	14:59	16:59
Malmö	13:57	15:57	17:57

(a) What is the latest time she can leave Göteborg?

Answer .... *(1 mark)*

(b) How long will her journey take?

....

Answer .... hours ....mins *(2 marks)*

Shape, Space & Measures

S23 Each square has an area of 1 cm².

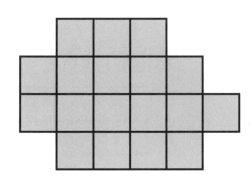

(a) Find the area, in cm², of the shape.

....

Answer .... cm² *(1 mark)*

(b) Find the perimeter, in cm, of the shape.

....

Answer .... cm *(1 mark)*

S24 Find the area of the shape below. Each square represents an area of 1 m².

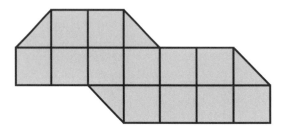

....

Area = ... m² *(1 mark)*

S25 **(a)** Determine the perimeter of this shape:

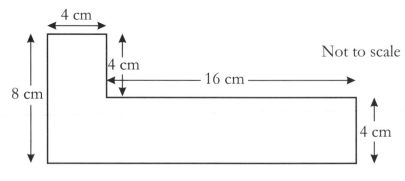

....

....

Answer .... cm *(2 marks)*

(b) Work out the area of the shape.

....

....

Answer .... cm² *(3 marks)*

S26 **(a)** Find the perimeter of the shape below.

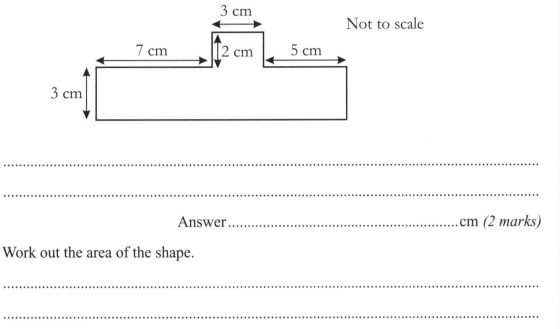

Not to scale

....

....

Answer...cm *(2 marks)*

(b) Work out the area of the shape.

....

....

Answer...cm² *(3 marks)*

S27 Find the areas of the following triangles.

(a)

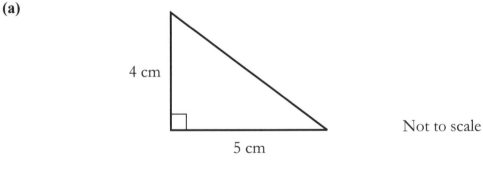

Not to scale

....

Answer... cm² *(1 mark)*

(b)

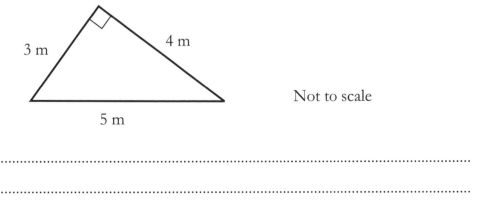

Not to scale

....

....

Answer... m² *(2 marks)*

Shape, Space & Measures

PERIMETER & AREA

S28 The area of a triangle is 8 m².
Change 8 m² to cm².

....

....

Answer...cm² *(2 marks)*

S29 A triangular hole is punched out of a rectangular piece of card.

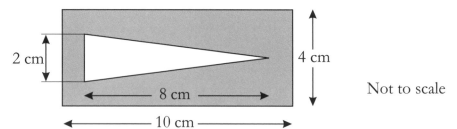

Not to scale

(a) Work out the area of the triangular hole.

....

Answer..cm² *(1 mark)*

(b) Work out the area of the remaining card.

....

....

Answer...cm² *(2 marks)*

S30

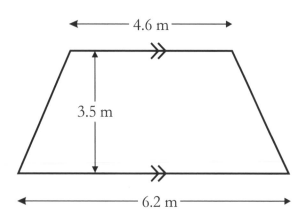

Not to scale

Calculate the area of the trapezium above.
State your units.

....

....

Answer... *(2 marks)*

S31 This circle has a diameter of 6 cm.

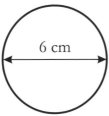

6 cm

Not accurately drawn

(a) Work out the circumference of the circle.
Give your answer correct to 1 decimal place.

....

....

Answer ....cm *(2 marks)*

(b) Work out the area of the circle.
Give your answer correct to 1 decimal place.

....

....

....

Answer ....cm² *(2 marks)*

S32 **(a)** A circular helicopter landing pad has a radius of 5 m.
What is the circumference of the helicopter landing pad?
Give your answer correct to 1 decimal place.

....

....

Answer ....m *(2 marks)*

(b) Calculate the area of a semicircle with radius 7 cm.
Give your answer correct to 1 decimal place.

7 cm

Not accurately drawn

....

....

....

Answer ....cm² *(3 marks)*

Shape, Space & Measures

CIRCLES

S33 What is the perimeter of the semicircular shape shown?
Leave your answer in terms of π.

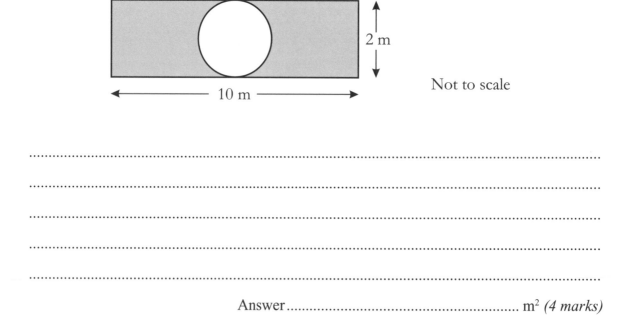

← 6 cm →

Not accurately drawn

....

....

....

....

Answer...cm *(3 marks)*

S34 Find the area of the shaded part of this shape.
Leave your answer in terms of π.

2 m

← 10 m →

Not to scale

....

....

....

....

....

Answer... m² *(4 marks)*

S35 Below is a solid made from centimetre cubes.

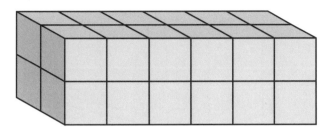

(a) What is the total surface area of the shape?

....

....

Answer..cm² *(2 marks)*

(b) What is the volume of the shape?

....

....

Answer..cm³ *(2 marks)*

S36 The shape below is made from cubes of side 1 cm.

(a) What is the total surface area of the shape?

....

....

Answer..cm² *(2 marks)*

(b) Calculate the volume of the shape.

....

....

Answer..cm³ *(2 marks)*

Shape, Space & Measures

VOLUME & SURFACE AREA

S37 Find the volume of this cuboid.

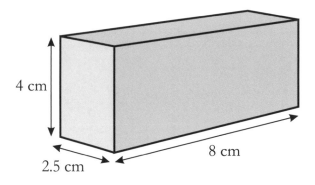

4 cm

2.5 cm

8 cm

Not to scale

....

....

Answer...cm³ *(2 marks)*

S38 **(a)** Find the volume of this cuboid.

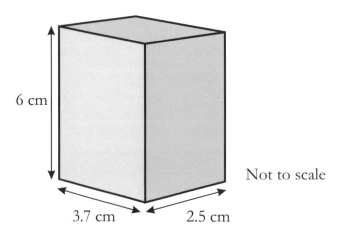

6 cm

3.7 cm

2.5 cm

Not to scale

....

....

Answer...cm³ *(2 marks)*

(b) What is the total surface area of the cuboid?

....

....

....

....

Answer...cm² *(3 marks)*

Shape, Space & Measures

VOLUME & SURFACE AREA

S39 (a) Calculate the area of this triangle.

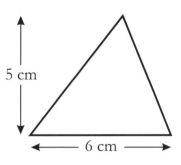

5 cm

6 cm

Not to scale

....

Answer .... cm² *(1 mark)*

(b) A triangular prism, based on the triangle above, has a depth of 20 cm.
What is the volume of the triangular prism?

....

....

Answer ....cm³ *(2 marks)*

S40 A triangular-prism shaped box has dimensions as shown in the diagram.

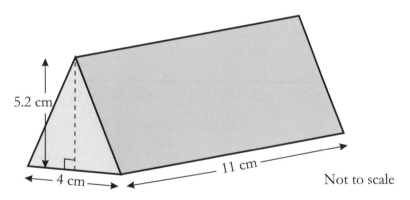

5.2 cm

4 cm

11 cm

Not to scale

Calculate the volume of the box.

....

....

....

Answer ....cm³ *(3 marks)*

Shape, Space & Measures

VOLUME & SURFACE AREA

S41 A cylinder has dimensions as shown below.

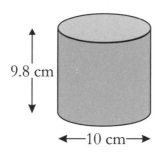

9.8 cm

Not to scale

←—10 cm—→

(a) Calculate the total surface area of the cylinder.
Give your answer to the nearest whole number.

....

....

....

....

....

Answer...cm^2 *(5 marks)*

(b) Calculate the volume of the cylinder.
Give your answer correct to 1 decimal place.

....

....

....

....

Answer...cm^3 *(4 marks)*

S42 The volume of a cylinder is 417 cm^3.
Change 417 cm^3 to mm^3.

....

....

Answer.. mm^3 *(2 marks)*

Shape, Space & Measures

S43 A vet weighed a dog on scales that were accurate to the nearest kilogram.
The display showed the dog's weight as 32 kg.

    (a) What is the minimum that the dog could have weighed?

        Answer .... kg *(1 mark)*

    (b) What is the upper bound for the dog's weight?

        Answer .... kg *(1 mark)*

S44 A javelin was thrown 54 m to the nearest metre.

    (a) What is the minimum distance that the javelin could have been thrown?

        Answer .... m *(1 mark)*

    (b) What is the upper bound for the distance the javelin could have been thrown?

        Answer .... m *(1 mark)*

S45 **(a)** Measure and write down the size of angle x.

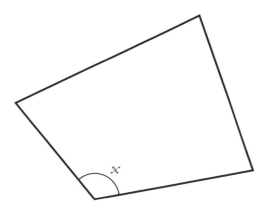

        Answer $x =$ .... degrees *(1 mark)*

    (b) Which of these correctly describe angle x:

        right angle, obtuse angle, reflex angle or acute angle?

        Answer .... *(1 mark)*

Shape, Space & Measures

S46 How many degrees are there in:

(a) half a turn?

....

Answer .... degrees *(1 mark)*

(b) $\frac{2}{3}$ of a right angle?

....

Answer ....degrees *(2 marks)*

(c) 0.6 of a right angle?

....

Answer ....degrees *(2 marks)*

S47 (a) Without measuring, work out the size of the angle marked *a*.

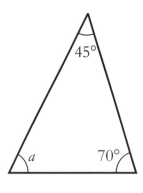

Not to scale

....

....

Answer *a* = ...degrees *(2 marks)*

(b) Work out the size of the angle marked *b*.

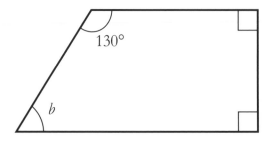

Not to scale

....

....

Answer *b* = ...degrees *(2 marks)*

Shape, Space & Measures

S48

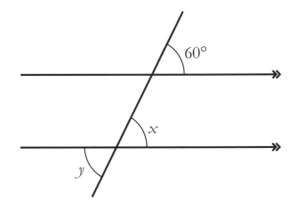

Not to scale

(a) Explain why angle x is 60°.

....

.... *(1 mark)*

(b) Write down the size of angle y.

Answer y = ... degrees *(1 mark)*

S49

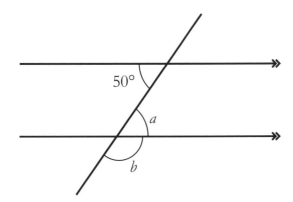

Not to scale

(a) Explain why angle a is 50°.

....

.... *(1 mark)*

(b) What is the size of angle b?

....

Answer b = ... degrees *(1 mark)*

Shape, Space & Measures

S50

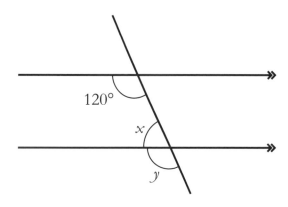

Not to scale

(a) Explain why angle *x* is 60°.

....

.... *(1 mark)*

(b) What is the size of angle *y*?

....

Answer *y* = ... degrees *(1 mark)*

S51

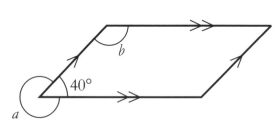

Not to scale

(a) Explain why angle *a* is 320°.

....

.... *(1 mark)*

(b) What is the size of angle *b*?

....

Answer *b* = ... degrees *(1 mark)*

S52 The diagram shows part of a regular polygon.

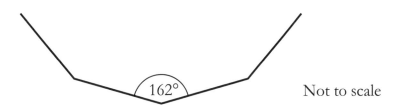

162°   Not to scale

(a) What size is the exterior angle of the polygon?

....

....

Answer..degrees *(2 marks)*

(b) How many sides does the complete polygon have?

....

....

Answer..*(2 marks)*

S53 *LMNOP* is a regular pentagon.

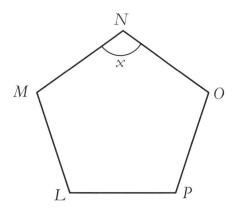

N

x

M   O

L   P   Not to scale

(a) Work out the sum of the interior angles of a pentagon.

....

....

Answer..degrees *(2 marks)*

(b) Calculate the size of angle *x*.

....

Answer *x* = ...degrees *(1 mark)*

Shape, Space & Measures

POLYGONS

S54 The diagram shows a regular heptagon.

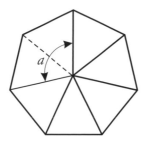

Not to scale

Calculate the size of angle *a*.
Give your answer to the nearest degree.

....

....

Answer *a* =..degrees *(2 marks)*

S55 **(a)** Calculate the sum of the interior angles of a hexagon.

....

....

Answer..degrees *(2 marks)*

(b) Work out the size of the angles marked *x*.

140°

120°

x

x

130°

Not to scale

....

....

Answer *x* =..degrees *(2 marks)*

S56 Calculate the length *AB* correct to one decimal place.

Not to scale

B

3 cm

A   5 cm   *C*

....

....

....

Answer..cm *(3 marks)*

S57 Find the length *LN*.
Give your answer to 1 d.p.

M

Not to scale

6.7 m

14.3 m

L   *N*

....

....

....

Answer..m *(3 marks)*

S58 Find the length *AB*.
Give your answer to 1 d.p.

B   4.9 cm   *C*

7.4 cm

Not to scale

A

....

....

....

Answer..m *(3 marks)*

Shape, Space & Measures

S59

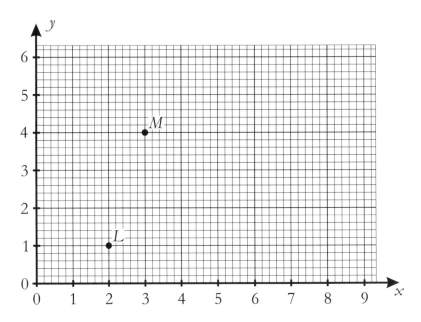

(a) What are the coordinates of these points?

    (i) L Answer (........................, ...) *(1 mark)*

    (ii) M Answer (........................, ...) *(1 mark)*

(b) On the same grid, plot and label the points:

    (i) $N\,(8, 4)$ *(1 mark)*

    (ii) $O\,(7, 1)$ *(1 mark)*

(c) What is the mathematical name for the shape *LMNO*?

                                Answer .... *(1 mark)*

S60

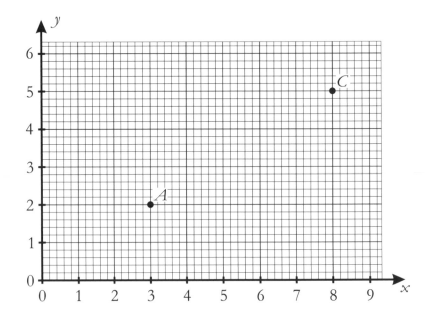

(a) What are the coordinates of these points?

    (i) A Answer (........................, ...) *(1 mark)*

    (ii) C Answer (........................, ...) *(1 mark)*

(b) On the same grid, plot and label these points.

    (i)   *B* (3, 5)   *(1 mark)*

    (ii)   *D* (8, 2)   *(1 mark)*

(c) What is the area of the shape *ABCD*?

....

Answer...cm² *(2 marks)*

S61 The line segment *AB* goes from *A* (2, 3) to *B* (5, –1).
Point *C* has the coordinates (4, –2).

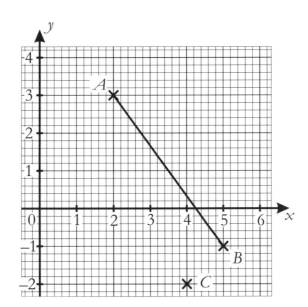

(a) Work out the coordinates of the mid-point of *AB*.

....

....

....

Answer (..........................., ...) *(3 marks)*

(b) Another point, *D*, is plotted so that the shape *ABCD* is a rectangle.
Find the coordinates of the point *D*.

....

Answer (..........................., ...) *(2 marks)*

Shape, Space & Measures

Similar Shapes

S62 These triangles are similar.

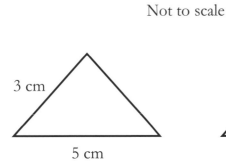

Not to scale

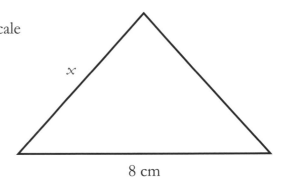

Find the length *x*.

....

....

....

Answer *x* = ...cm *(2 marks)*

S63

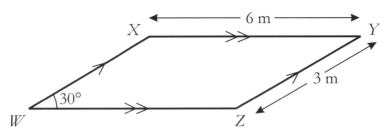

Not to scale

The parallelogram above is enlarged so that *XY* becomes 9 m.

(a) Calculate the new length of the side *ZY*.

....

....

....

Answer...m *(2 marks)*

(b) What is the size of angle *WXY* in the enlarged parallelogram?

....

....

Answer... degrees *(1 mark)*

S64 The diagram shows a rough sketch of an island.
Junmouth is due east of Ruston.

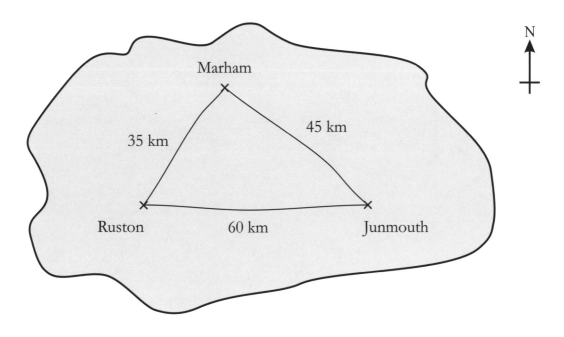

Using ruler and compasses only, make an accurate map of the island.
Use a scale of 1 cm to represent 10 km.
You **must** show clearly all your construction arcs.

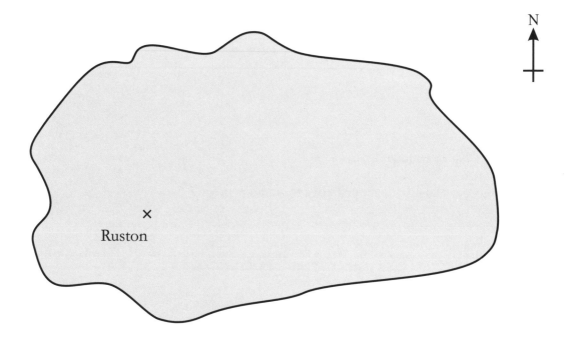

(3 marks)

Shape, Space & Measures

SCALE DRAWINGS & BEARINGS

S65 The diagram shows the positions of two marker buoys *A* and *B*.

The scale is 1 cm to 10 km.

(a) What is the real-life distance between *A* and *B* in km?

....

Answer..km *(2 marks)*

(b) What is the bearing of *B* from *A*?

Answer... *(1 mark)*

(c) A racing yacht (*C*) is anchored 50 km south of *A*.
Mark accurately the position of *C* on the diagram.

....*(2 marks)*

S66 Below is a scale drawing of two boats at sea.
Boat Q is due south of boat P.

N

$\times$ P

$\times$ Q

The scale of the drawing is 1 cm to 100 m.

(a) How far in real life is boat P from boat Q?

....

Answer ....m *(2 marks)*

(b) Mark on the diagram the position of boat R, which is 1000 m from P on a bearing of
120°.

....*(2 marks)*

Shape, Space & Measures

S67 The diagram shows the positions of three shapes, *L*, *M* and *N*.

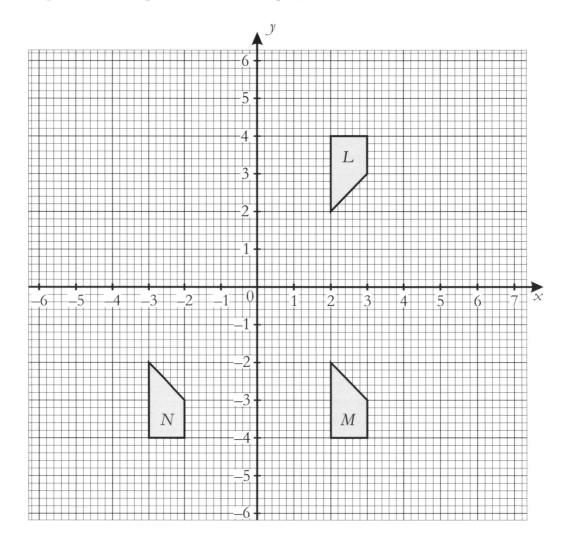

(a) Describe the transformation that moves *L* onto *M*.

....

....*(2 marks)*

(b) Describe the transformation that moves *M* onto *N*.

....

....*(2 marks)*

S68 The diagram shows the positions of two shapes *A* and *B*.

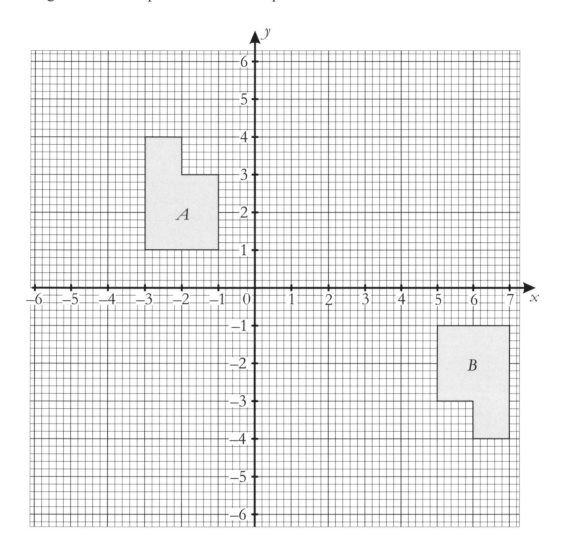

(a) Describe a single transformation that takes *A* onto *B*.

....

....*(2 marks)*

Shape *A* is reflected in the *x*-axis.

(b) Draw the new position of *A*. Label it *C*.   *(1 mark)*

(c) Describe a transformation that takes *C* onto *B*.

....

....*(2 marks)*

Shape, Space & Measures

S69 **(a)** Draw an enlargement of shape *LMNOPQ* with scale factor 3.

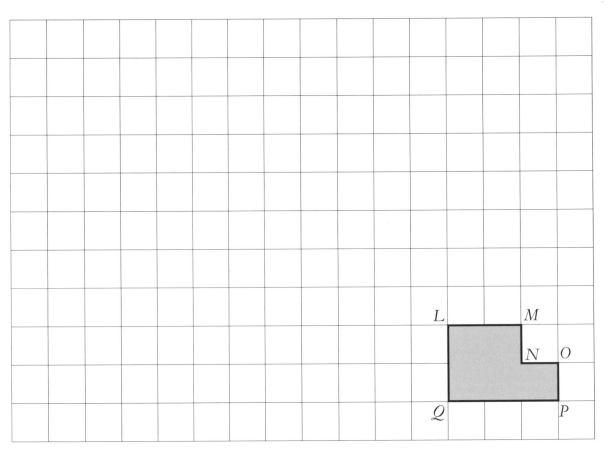

(3 marks)

(b) Is the enlarged shape that you have drawn congruent to shape *LMNOPQ*? Explain your answer.

....

....*(2 marks)*

S70 Draw the enlargement of triangle *ABC* with centre *O* and scale factor 2.

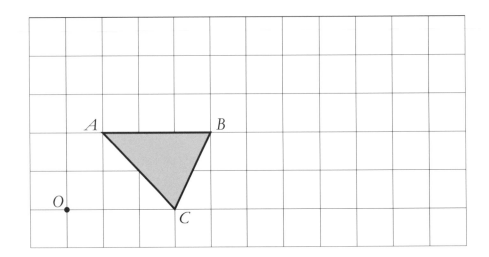

(3 marks)

Shape, Space & Measures

S71   I once ran the 400 m in 50 seconds.
What was my average speed in metres per second?

....

....

Answer.. m/s *(2 marks)*

S72   A car travelled 182 miles in 3.5 hours.
What was the average speed in miles per hour?

....

....

Answer..mph *(2 marks)*

S73   How far would a train, travelling at an average speed of 62 km/h, travel in one and a half hours?

....

....

Answer..km *(2 marks)*

S74   A piece of metal has a mass of 5004 kg and a volume of 1.2 m^3.
Calculate the density of the metal.

....

....

Answer.. kg/m^3 *(2 marks)*

S75   25 tonnes of soil is removed from a field in order to turn it into a golf course.

(a)   How many kilograms is 25 tonnes?

....

Answer.. kg *(1 mark)*

The soil has a density of 200 kg/m^3.

(b)   What volume of soil is removed from the field?

....

....

Answer.. m^3 *(2 marks)*

Handling Data

MEAN, MEDIAN, MODE, RANGE

H1 **(a)** Katherine measures the diameters of some <u>beef</u> tomatoes.
The diameters, in millimetres, are:

$$80, 82, 82, 83, 85, 89, 91, 92, 92, 94$$

(i) What is the range of the diameters of the beef tomatoes?

Answer...1 4 ✓ ....mm *(1 mark)*

(ii) What is the mean diameter of the beef tomatoes?

870 ÷ 10

Answer..... 8.7 ✓✓✓ mm *(3 marks)*

To compare, Katherine measures the diameters of some <u>plum</u> tomatoes.
The range of these diameters is 18 mm and the mean 62 mm.

(b) Use the range and mean to compare these two varieties.

range = 44 mm   mean = 71 mm

....*(2 marks)*

H2 **(a)** Younis weighs some English Red apples.
The weights, in grams, are listed below.

$$55, 56, 56, 57, 59, 60, 62, 63, 63, 64, 65$$

(i) What is the range of weights for the English Red apples?

Answer...1 0 ✓ .... g *(1 mark)*

(ii) What is the mean weight of the English Red apples?

660 ÷ 11

Answer. 60 ✓✓✓ g *(3 marks)*

Younis then weighs some South African Green apples.
The range of these weights is 16 g and the mean is 60 g.

(b) Use the range and mean to compare these two varieties of apples.

range = 16   s > to 68.

mean =

....*(2 marks)*

8

Handling Data

H3 The weights of 9 badminton players are shown below.

75 kg, 81 kg, 74 kg, 84 kg, 74 kg, 78 kg, 83 kg, 74 kg, 83 kg

(a) Find their median weight.

74, 74, 74, 75, 78, 81, 82, 83, 84

Answer 78 ✓✓ kg *(2 marks)*

(b) Find the mode of their weights.

Answer 74 ✓ kg *(1 mark)*

(c) Which of **(a)** and **(b)** is not a good indicator of their average weight? Why?

I think a is the best one because it shows a bigger value than B. ✓ *(1 mark)*

H4 Luke carried out a survey of how much money 8 of his friends had deposited in their savings accounts. The amounts were £47, £55, £63, £57, £82, £4002, £55 and £12.

(a) What was the mean amount deposited? 12, 47, 55, 55, 57, 63,

4373 ÷ 8   82, 4002

Answer £ 546.625 *(3 marks)*

(b) Find the median.

Answer £ 56 ✓✓ *(2 marks)*

(c) Look at your answers to **(a)** and **(b)**. Which does not give a good indication of the average savings of the 8 friends? Explain your answer.

(1 mark)

6

Handling Data

H5

	Balcony	No Balcony	Totals
Men	18	27	45
Women	2̶7̶	26	47
Children	37	48	85
Totals	76	101	177

There are 177 people staying at a hotel, 101 of whom are staying in a room with no balcony.

(a) Complete the two-way frequency table above. ✓✓ *(2 marks)*

(b) How many women are staying in rooms with a balcony?

Answer .... 21 ✓ .... *(1 mark)*

H6

	$h \leqslant 5$ ft	5 ft $< h < 6$ ft	$h \geqslant 6$ ft	Totals
Men	3	8	5	16
Women	5	9	2	16
Totals	8	2̶7̶	7	32

The two-way frequency table shows some data on the heights (h) of 32 men and women.

(a) Complete the table. *(2 marks)*

(b) How many of the men are 6 ft or over?

Answer .... 7 .... *(1 mark)*

H7 The table shows the number of eggs laid by 100 different hens.

Number of Eggs	Number of Hens
0	18
1	32
2	26
3	12
4	8
5	4

(a) What is the modal number of eggs laid?

Answer .... 1 .... *(1 mark)*

(b) What is the median number of eggs laid?

add them all up and divide with the number of hens.

Answer .16. .... *(2 marks)*

(c) Calculate the mean number of eggs laid per hen.

Its inbetween 2 and 3 therefore its 2.5 .

Answer 2.5 .... *(4 marks)*

H8 The frequency table below shows the number of goals scored by 40 non-league football teams one Saturday afternoon.

Number of Goals	Number of Teams
0	11
1	13
2	9
3	5
4	2

(a) Calculate the mean number of goals scored per team.

....

....

....

Answer .... *(4 marks)*

(b) What is the modal number of goals scored per team?

Answer .... *(1 mark)*

Handling Data

FREQUENCY TABLES

H9 Joe carried out a survey to find out how long people spent cleaning their teeth in the morning.

Time (*t* seconds)	Number
$0 < t \leqslant 20$	4
$20 < t \leqslant 40$	17
$40 < t \leqslant 60$	15
$60 < t \leqslant 80$	10
$80 < t \leqslant 100$	3

(a) Write down the modal class.

Answer .... *(1 mark)*

(b) Which class contains the median?
Explain how you found your answer.

Class ....

because ....

....*(2 marks)*

(c) Estimate the mean time these people spent cleaning their teeth.
Give your answer to the nearest second.

....

....

....

Answer .... seconds *(4 marks)*

BAR CHARTS

H10 The bar chart below shows the number of hours that Bushra spent listening to music during one week.

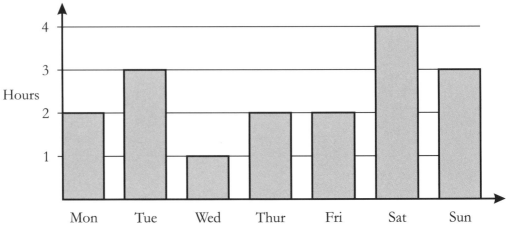

86

(a) On which day did she spend the least amount of time listening to music?

Answer .... *(1 mark)*

(b) How many hours did she spend listening to music in total during the week?

....

....

Answer ....hours *(2 marks)*

H11 Toni carried out a survey in her street.
She asked which households kept a dog (D), a cat (C), a bird (B) or no pet (N).
The raw data is shown below.

D C D B N C D N C D N
B C N D D D N C B C N

(a) Complete the frequency table. *(2 marks)*

Type of Pet	Dog	Cat	Bird	No Pet
Tally	卌 ‖			
Frequency	7			

(b) Complete the bar chart to illustrate Toni's data. *(2 marks)*

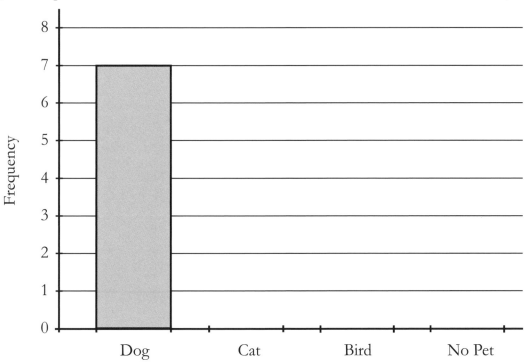

Handling Data

H12 The pictogram shows the number of barges moored overnight at a harbour during one week.

Number of barges moored overnight

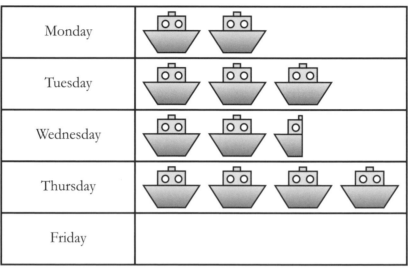

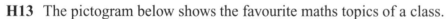 represents 10 barges

(a) How many barges were moored at the harbour on:

(i) Tuesday night?

Answer.. *(1 mark)*

(ii) Wednesday night?

Answer.. *(1 mark)*

On Friday, 35 barges were moored at the harbour.

(b) Complete the pictogram to show Friday's data. *(1 mark)*

H13 The pictogram below shows the favourite maths topics of a class.

Number	우 우 우
Algebra	우 우
Shape, Space & Measures	우 우 우 우
Handling Data	

우 represents 2 people

(a) How many students said their favourite topic was Number?

Answer.. *(1 mark)*

(b) Five students said that Handling Data was their favourite topic.
Use this information to complete the pictogram. *(1 mark)*

(c) How many students are there in the maths class?

....

Answer...*(2 marks)*

H14 The heights of some flowers are
displayed in the frequency table.

Height (*h* cm)	Number
$0 < h \leqslant 5$	3
$5 < h \leqslant 10$	7
$10 < h \leqslant 15$	9
$15 < h \leqslant 20$	5
$20 < h \leqslant 25$	4

(a) Write down the modal class.

Answer... *(1 mark)*

(b) Show these heights in a frequency diagram. *(3 marks)*

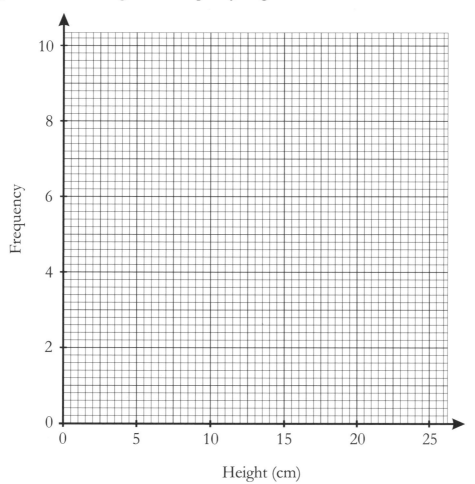

Height (cm)

Handling Data

H15 Imran timed how long his racing pigeons took to return home after being released some distance away. His data, in minutes, is recorded below.

43	30	50	55	46	37	52	47	41	49
53	44	49	43	50	41	59	45	48	47
47	40	45	58	33	34	42	49	36	43

(a) Complete the grouped frequency table for the times.

Time (T mins)	Tally	Frequency
$30 \leqslant T < 36$		
$36 \leqslant T < 42$		
$42 \leqslant T < 48$		
$48 \leqslant T < 54$		
$54 \leqslant T < 60$		

(3 marks)

(b) Draw a frequency diagram for the times on the graph paper below.

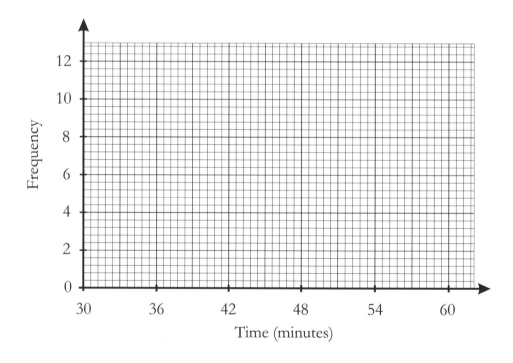

(3 marks)

H16 These are the marks obtained by 20 pupils in a science test.

13 42 34 20 24 42 26 29 30 49
33 14 36 38 23 26 42 46 48 31

(a) Show this information in an ordered stem and leaf diagram.

```
1 |
  |
2 |
  |
3 |
  |
4 |
```

Key 3|4 represents a mark of 34

(3 marks)

(b) What is the mode for the data?

Answer .... *(1 mark)*

(c) What is the median?

....

....

Answer .... *(2 marks)*

H17 Below are the number of shots taken by 24 golfers in the final round of a tournament.

64 87 67 68 95 91 70 83 72 71 73 90
72 64 72 71 65 72 68 81 70 87 69 89

(a) Draw an ordered stem and leaf diagram for the data.

```
 |
 |
 |
 |
 |
```

Key 6|7 represents 67 shots

(3 marks)

(b) The median of the scores in the final round is to become the new par for the course.
What is the new par for the course?

....

....

Answer .... *(2 marks)*

Handling Data

PIE CHARTS

H18 A mobile phone manufacturer makes covers in five colours.
The pie chart shows the colour distribution of 900 covers sold.

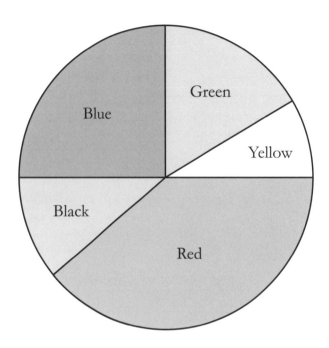

(a) Measure the angle for yellow.

Answer .... degrees *(1 mark)*

(b) What fraction of the covers sold were yellow?
Write your fraction in its lowest terms.

....

Answer .... *(1 mark)*

(c) How many yellow covers were sold?

....

....

Answer .... *(2 marks)*

(d) How many of the covers sold were red?

....

....

....

....

Answer .... *(4 marks)*

H19 John carried out a survey of 60 pupils in his year at school.
He wanted to know how many books they had each bought in the last year.
The frequency table shows his data.

Number of books	Frequency	Angle of Sector
0 to 2	12	
3 to 5	32	
6 to 8	11	
9 or more	5	

(a) Construct a pie chart to show this information.

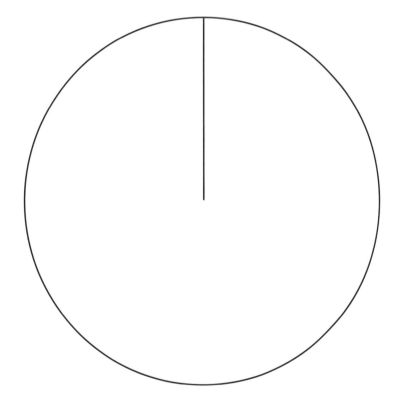

(5 marks)

(b) What fraction of the pupils bought 3, 4 or 5 books?
Write your fraction in its lowest terms.

....

....

Answer ....*(2 marks)*

Handling Data

H20 On a certain day last year, an automobile factory produced 180 vans.
The table below shows the colours of the vans.

Colour	White	Red	Blue	Grey	
Number	88	22	18	52	**Total**
Angle					360°

(a) By first completing the table above, construct a pie chart in the circle below.

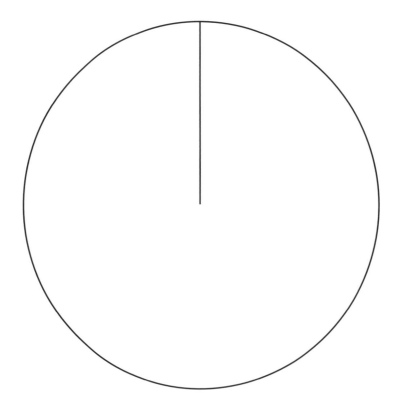

(5 marks)

(b) What fraction of the vans were blue?
Write your fraction in its lowest terms.

....

....

Answer ....*(2 marks)*

H21 The time series graph shows the temperature, in degrees Celsius, at midday during the last ten days of March in Barrow-in-Furness.

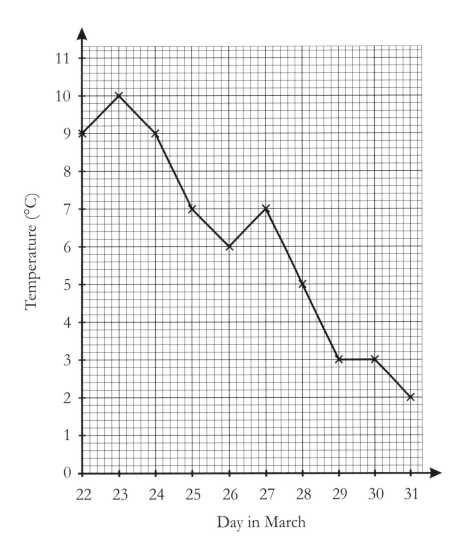

(a) On which day was the highest temperature recorded?

Answer .... *(1 mark)*

(b) Which day had the same temperature as the previous day?

Answer .... *(1 mark)*

(c) Sandra predicts that the temperature on the 1st of April will be 1°C.
Give a reason why Sandra might be wrong.

....

.... *(1 mark)*

Handling Data

H22 The table shows the number of employees working for a walking boot manufacturer over a three-year period.

	March	June	September	December
2004	68	78	72	42
2005	62	72	75	38
2006	57	64	68	36

(a) On the grid below, draw a line graph of the data.
The data for 2004 has been plotted for you.

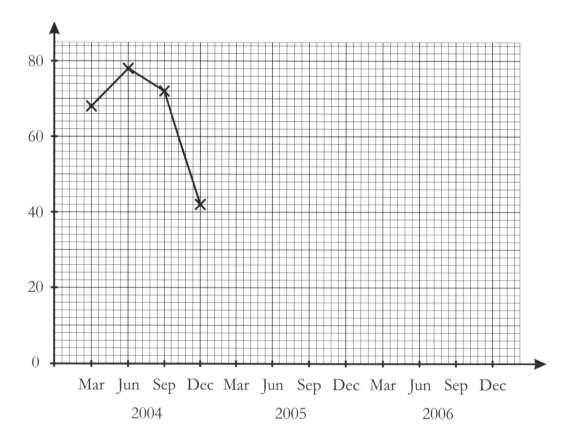

(2 marks)

(b) In which month of which year was the number of employees highest?

Answer .... *(1 mark)*

(c) In which month of which year was the number of employees lowest?

Answer .... *(1 mark)*

H23 The table shows the prices of nine cars, together with their top speeds in mph.

Price (£1000s)	12	26	32	15	18	8	22	41	43
Top Speed (mph)	90	114	124	93	101	85	111	131	139

(a) On the grid below, draw a scatter graph to show this information.
The first five points have been plotted for you.

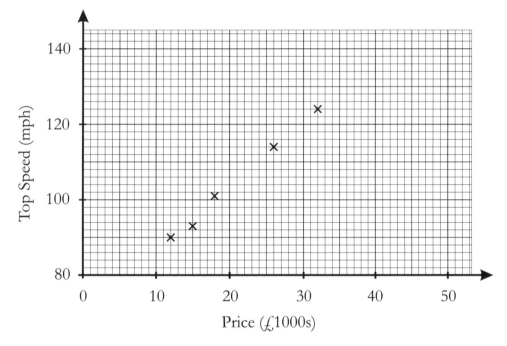

(2 marks)

(b) Describe the correlation between the prices of these cars and their top speeds.

.... *(1 mark)*

(c) Draw a line of best fit on your scatter graph. *(1 mark)*

(d) Use your line of best fit to estimate:

    (i) the price of a car with a top speed of 120 mph,

                Answer £.. *(1 mark)*

    (ii) the top speed of a car costing £25 000.

                Answer .... mph *(1 mark)*

Handling Data

H24 The table below shows the heights of some fully grown tomato plants and the amount of Thunder Growth Feed given to them each day.

Amount (ml)	23	8	10	22	14	15	21	12	19	16
Height (cm)	10	37	31	12	23	22	14	27	16	20

(a) On the grid below, draw a scatter graph to show this information.
The first four points have been plotted for you.

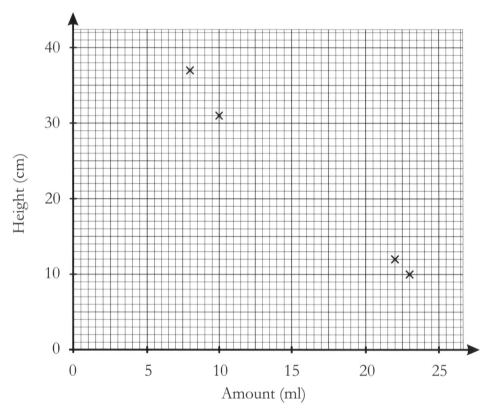

(3 marks)

(b) Describe the relationship shown by the scatter graph.

....

.... *(1 mark)*

(c) Draw a line of best fit on your scatter graph. *(1 mark)*

(d) Use your graph to roughly estimate the height of a fully grown tomato plant fed 20 ml of Thunder Growth Feed each day.

Answer.. cm *(1 mark)*

H25 Duncan has carried out some research into how the size of oak leaves varies with their position on the tree.

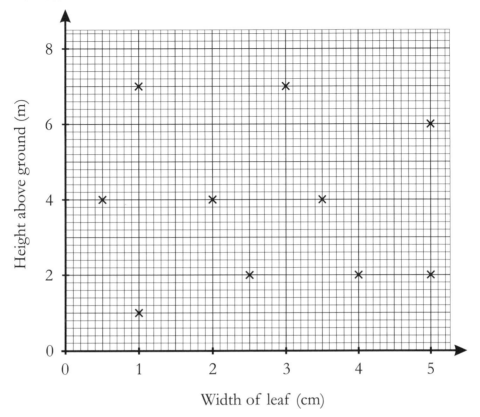

Explain why it is not possible to estimate the width of a leaf found 2 m above ground.

....

.... *(1 mark)*

H26 Cassy and Robert toss a coin to see who should go first in a board game.
What is the probability that the coin will land on heads?

....

Answer .... *(1 mark)*

H27 A letter is picked at random from the word CARPET.

What is the probability that the letter is:

(a) P?

....

Answer .... *(1 mark)*

(b) a vowel?

....

Answer .... *(1 mark)*

Handling Data

H28 This fair spinner is spun.

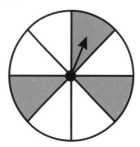

    (a)   **(i)**   Is it more likely to land on grey or white?

                  Answer .... *(1 mark)*

        (ii)   Give a reason for your answer.

              ....

              .... *(1 mark)*

    (b)   Mark the probability line below with a cross to show the probability that the spinner will land on grey.

0                              $\frac{1}{2}$ 1

                                                        (1 mark)

 H29 A bag contains 7 red balls and 8 blue balls.
A ball is taken from the bag at random.
Find the probability that the ball taken is:

    (a)   red,

      ....

                  Answer .... *(1 mark)*

    (b)   not red.

      ....

                  Answer .... *(1 mark)*

H30 A card is drawn at random from an ordinary pack of 52 playing cards.
What is the probability that it is:

(a) a spade?

....

Answer ....*(2 marks)*

(b) not a spade?

....

Answer .... *(1 mark)*

H31 An ordinary six-sided dice is rolled 240 times.

(a) How many times would you expect a 6 to be thrown?

....

....

Answer ....*(2 marks)*

(b) How many odd numbers would you expect to be thrown?

....

....

Answer ....*(2 marks)*

H32 A card was selected at random from an ordinary pack of 52 playing cards.
The card was then replaced and another card selected.
260 cards were selected in all.

(a) How many times would you expect a king to be picked?

....

....

Answer ....*(2 marks)*

(b) How many times would you expect a red queen to be picked?

....

....

Answer ....*(2 marks)*

Handling Data

H33 A bag contains red, green and black beads. If a bead is removed from the bag at random, the probability that it is red is 0.2 and the probability that it is green is 0.6.

(a) What is the probability of removing a black bead?

....

....

Answer...*(2 marks)*

There are 120 beads altogether in the bag.

(b) How many of the beads are green?

....

....

Answer...*(2 marks)*

H34 In a game, a fair coin is tossed and a fair six-sided dice rolled.
A head is worth 2 and a tail is worth 3.
This score is added to the number on the dice.

(a) Complete the table to show all possible scores.

		DICE					
	+	**1**	**2**	**3**	**4**	**5**	**6**
C O I N	**2**	3	4	5			
	3	4					

(1 mark)

(b) What is the probability that the score is:

(i) 5?

....

Answer...*(1 mark)*

(ii) greater than 6?

....

Answer...*(1 mark)*

(iii) 2?

....

Answer...*(1 mark)*

H35 The jack, queen and king from both the hearts and clubs suits are placed in two separate piles. One card is then taken from each pile.

(a) Complete the sample space diagram to show all the possible outcomes.

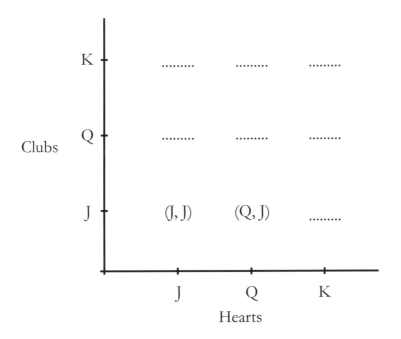

(2 marks)

(b) How many possible outcomes are there?

Answer.. *(1 mark)*

(c) What is the probability that both kings will be picked?

Answer.. *(1 mark)*

Handling Data

H36 Suna wants to find out how often people use public transport.
He has written three questions to use in a questionnaire.

> **1** What is your name? _____
>
> **2** Do you agree public transport is less convenient than using a car?
>
> ☐ yes ☐ no ☐ don't know
>
> **3** How many times a month do you use public transport?
>
> ☐ never ☐ hardly ever ☐ occasionally ☐ often

(a) What is wrong with the first question on the questionnaire?

....

.... *(1 mark)*

(b) What is wrong with Suna's second question?

....

.... *(1 mark)*

(c) What is wrong with the choices offered for the third question?
Explain how the choices could be improved.

....

....

.... *(1 mark)*

Answers

N1 (a) (i) 8157 (ii) 14 620

  (b) (i) thirteen thousand, six hundred and seven

   (ii) two hundred and eighty thousand, three hundred and one

N2 (a) 9, 23, 32, 33, 42, 46

  (b) 59, 479, 482, 497, 515, 517

N3 (a) 2 hundreds (200) (b) 2 thousands (2000)

  (c) 2 tenths (0.2)

N4 (a) 5 tens (50)

  (b) (i) 532 (ii) 235

N5 (a) 6, 24 (b) 25, 49 (c) 7, 19

N6 (a) 75 (b) 8 (c) 2

N7 (a) 332 (b) 471

N8 (a) 546 (b) 335

N9 672 pens

N10 31 safety marshals

N11 (a) 3, 9, 12 (b) 1, 3, 12

N12 (a) 2, 4, 6, 10 (b) 2, 10

N13 (a) 10, 30 (b) 1, 3

N14 (a) 14, 42 (b) 3, 6

N15 (a) 12 (b) 30

N16 (a) 3 (b) 13

N17 48

N18 6

N19 $\frac{4}{18}, \frac{18}{81}$

N20 $\frac{12}{14}, \frac{66}{77}, \frac{30}{35}$

N21 (a) (i) $\frac{1}{2}$ (ii) $\frac{1}{4}$

  (b) 18

N22 (a) (i) $\frac{2}{7}$ (ii) $\frac{1}{8}$

  (b) 24

N23 $\frac{1}{4}, \frac{2}{5}, \frac{3}{7}, \frac{2}{3}$

N24 $\frac{1}{2}, \frac{5}{11}, \frac{1}{3}, \frac{2}{7}$

N25 $\frac{24}{360} = \frac{1}{15}$

N26 $\frac{5}{30} = \frac{1}{6}$

N27 (a) $\frac{1}{5}$ (b) $\frac{3}{10}$ (c) 1

N28 (a) $\frac{4}{5}$ (b) $\frac{5}{8}$ (c) $\frac{2}{15}$

N29 $\frac{4}{5}$

N30 (a) 0.6

  (b) (i) 25 (ii) 0.0025

N31 $\frac{15}{100} = \frac{3}{20}$

N32 (a) 9.09 (b) 13.6

  (c) 23.5 (d) 4.72

N33 0.25 m

N34 9.1 kg

N35 0.7, $\frac{3}{4}, \frac{4}{5}$, 85%

N36 (a) 12 (b) 80

N37 (a) 17.5 (b) 6860

N38 (a) 0.7 (b) $\frac{3}{25}$ (c) 70%

N39 (a) 62.5% (b) 37.5%

N40 (a) £23 (b) £28.75

N41 (a) £10 200 (b) £8670

N42 12.9%

N43 23.8%

N44 7:1

N45 2:3:7

N46 £35

N47 £10

N48 £7.40

N49 £8.58

N50 120 g

N51 480 g

N52 (a) £5 (b) 26 golf balls

N53 (a) £82.32 (b) £10.29

N54 (a) 1432 units (b) £107.40

N55 (a) 6 packs (b) packs of 40

N56 The 750g pack is better value.

N57 (a) 125 (b) 81 (c) 6

N58 (a) 2.744 (b) 5.9

N59 (a) 9^5 (b) 9^2

N60 3.5 m

N61 6.5 cm

N62 (a) 252 (b) $2 \times 3^2 \times 5$

N63 $5^2 \times 11$

N64 (a) 9.2×10^5 (b) 43 000

N65 (a) 4.23×10^{-2} (b) 59 000 000

N66 2.3×10^8

N67 3.84×10^5 km

N68 (a) (i) 7 (ii) 14

  (b) (i) 180 (ii) 8580

N69 (a) (i) 10 200 (ii) 3400

  (b) (i) 14 000 (ii) 3000

N70 (a) 1.14 (b) 1.1

N71 $\frac{80 + 20}{30 - 10} = 5$

N72 $\frac{40 \times 10}{20 + 20} = 10$

N73 (a) 0.02163100075 (b) 0.022

N74 (a) 1.657586207 (b) 2

N75 (a) 258 m (b) 86 m

N76 (a) 24°C

  (b) Sweden –20°C
   France –5°C

N77 (a) –8, –5, –4, 3, 6 (b) –2, –1, 0, 1, 3

N78 (a) –10 (b) –2

  (c) –27 (d) –3

N79 (a) 2 (b) 2

  (c) 36 (d) 4

Answers

A1 (a) $p - 3$ (b) $c + 4$ (c) $2m$

A2 (a) $12ab$ (b) $3a^2$ (c) $a + 4b$

A3 (a) $x + 11y$ (b) a^6 (c) x^2

A4 (a) $x = 11$ (b) $x = 2$ (c) $x = 18$

A5 (a) $x = 8$ (b) $x = 7$ (c) $x = 16$

A6 (a) $x = 5$ (b) $x = 3$
     (c) $x = 3$ (d) $x = 8$

A7 (a) $x = \dfrac{2}{5}$ (b) $x = 4$
     (c) $x = 1$ (d) $x = 15$

A8 (a) 2 hours 55 mins   (b) 1.5 kg

A9 (a) $a = 15.8$ (b) $a = 16.6$

A10 (a) $p = 5$ (b) $p = -1$ (c) $p = -37$

A11 (a) $C = 5$ (b) $C = 30$ (c) $C = 65$

A12 (a) $A = 27$ (b) $A = 37$ (c) $A = 121$

A13 (a) $T = 20W + 20$ (b) 3 hours

A14 (a) $P = 6H + 2S$ (b) £412

A15 (a) $n = \dfrac{m + 1}{5}$ (b) $q = \sqrt{p - 2}$

A16 (a) $b = \dfrac{a}{2c^2}$ (b) $c = \sqrt{\dfrac{a}{2b}}$

A17 (a)

x	-2	-1	0	1	2	3
$y = 2x + 2$	-2	0	2	4	6	8

(b)

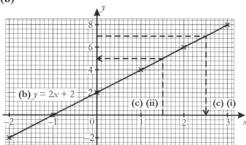

(c) (i) $x = 2.5$ (ii) $y = 5$

A18 (a)

x	-2	-1	0	1	2	3
$y = 2x - 2$	-6	-4	-2	0	2	4

(b)

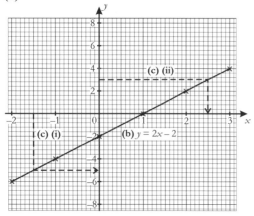

(c) (i) $y = -5$ (ii) $x = 2.5$

A19 $y = 2x + 18$

A20 (a)

x	0	1	2	3
$y = 2x$	0	2	4	6

(b)

x	0	1	2	3
$y = 6 - x$	6	5	4	3

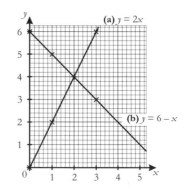

(c) (2, 4)

A21 $-5, -4, -3, -2, -1, 0, 1, 2, 3$

A22 $-1, 0, 1, 2, 3, 4, 5, 6$

A23 (a)

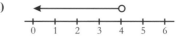

(b)

A24 (a) $x < \dfrac{1}{2}$ (b) $x > 3$

A25 $x = 7.9$ to 1 d.p.

A26 $x = 3.2$ to 1 d.p.

A27 (a) $7a + 21$ (b) $3(3b - 2)$

A28 (a) $6m + 11n$ (b) $5x(x - 2)$

A29 $x^2 + 5x + 6$

A30 $3x^2 + x - 2$

A31 (a)

x	-2	-1	0	1	2
$y = x^2 + 2$	6	3	2	3	6

(b)

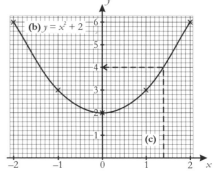

(c) $y = 4$

A32 (a)

x	0	1	2	3
x^2	0	1	4	9
$y = 3x^2$	0	3	12	27

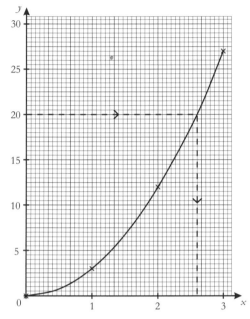

(b) $x = 2.6$

A33 (a) 11:20   (b) 10 minutes   (c) 2.5 km

(d)

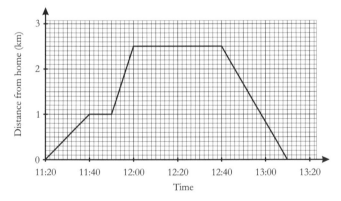

A34 (a) 16 km   (b) 6 km   (c) 0 km/min

A35 (a) C\$40   (b) £50

A36 (a) 176°F   (b) 38°C

A37 Vase A matches graph 4.
Vase B matches graph 3.
Vase C matches graph 2.
Vase D matches graph 1.

A38 (a)

Pattern	1	2	3	4
Number of Squares	1	5	9	13

(b) 17   (c) 37

A39 (a)

Pattern	1	2	3	4	5
Number of Squares	1	3	5	7	9

(b) By adding 2 more squares to the previous number of squares.

(c) 17

A40 (a) 17, 20

(b) Each term is 3 more than the previous one.

(c) 26

(d) $3n + 2$

A41 (a) 15

(b) Each term is 2 more than the previous one.

(c) 19

(d) $2n + 7$

A42 (a) 15, 21   (b) Triangular numbers

A43 (a) 25, 36   (b) Square numbers

SHAPE, SPACE & MEASURES

S1 (a) rectangle   (b) parallelogram

(c) regular pentagon

S2 (a) square   (b) equilateral triangle

(c) kite

S3 (a) (i) cone   (ii) cuboid

(b) (i) 12   (ii) 8   (iii) 6

S4 (a) (i) cylinder (ii) square-based pyramid

(b) (i) 8   (ii) 5   (iii) 5

S5 cube

S6 cuboid

S7

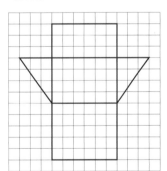

Other nets are possible.

S8

Front elevation (F)	Side elevation (S)

Answers

S9 (a) cube and cylinder (b)

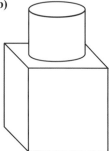

S10

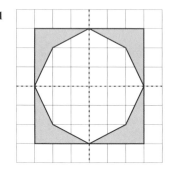

S11

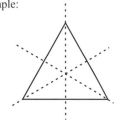

S12 (a) 2   (b) 2
    (c) 4   (d) 8

S13 (a) Z
    (b) For example:

S14 (a) (i) 3.5 cm
       (ii)

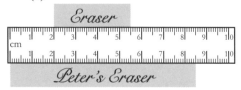

    (b) 4 cm

S15 (a) (i) 1.1 kg (ii)

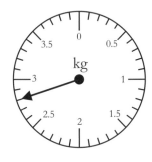

    (b) 7.2 cm
S16 (a) 3.52 m   (b) 1600 g   (c) 40 lb
S17 (a) 450 cm   (b) 25 000 g   (c) 17.5 pints
S18 (a) metre   (b) about 12 m   (c) about 800 g
    (d) about 8 oz   (e) about 9 litres   (f) about 0.5 pint
S19 $25 \times 5 \div 8 = 15.625$ miles
S20 $10 \times 4 \div 7 = 5.7$ litres
S21 (a) 11:15   (b) 1 hour 35 mins
S22 (a) 14:42   (b) 3 hours 15 mins
S23 (a) 18 cm²   (b) 20 cm
S24 14 m²
S25 (a) 56 cm   (b) 96 cm²
S26 (a) 40 cm   (b) 51 cm²
S27 (a) 10 cm²   (b) 6 m²
S28 80 000 cm²
S29 (a) 8 cm²   (b) 32 cm²
S30 18.9 m²
S31 (a) 18.8 cm   (b) 28.3 cm²
S32 (a) 31.4 m   (b) 77.0 cm²
S33 $(3\pi + 6)$ cm
S34 $(20 - \pi)$ m²
S35 (a) 56 cm²   (b) 24 cm³
S36 (a) 70 cm²   (b) 24 cm³
S37 80 cm³
S38 (a) 55.5 cm³   (a) 92.9 cm²
S39 (a) 15 cm²   (b) 300 cm³
S40 114.4 cm³
S41 (a) $2\pi rh + 2\pi r^2 = 465$ cm²
    (b) $\pi r^2 h = 769.7$ cm³
S42 417 000 mm³
S43 (a) 31.5 kg   (b) 32.5 kg
S44 (a) 53.5 m   (b) 54.5 m
S45 (a) $x = 120°$ (b) obtuse angle
S46 (a) 180°   (b) 60°   (c) 54°
S47 (a) 65°   (b) 50°
S48 (a) x and 60° are corresponding angles and so are equal.
    (b) 60°
S49 (a) a and 50° are alternate angles and so are equal.
    (b) 130°
S50 (a) x and 120° are supplementary angles and so add up to 180°.
    (b) 120°

S51 **(a)** Angles at a point add up to 360°, so
$a + 40° = 360°$.

(b) 140°

S52 **(a)** 18° **(b)** 20 sides

S53 **(a)** (number of sides – 2) × 180° = 540°

(b) 108°

S54 103°

S55 **(a)** (number of sides – 2) × 180° = 720°

(b) 120°

S56 5.8 cm

S57 12.6 m

S58 5.5 cm

S59 **(a)** **(i)** (2, 1) **(ii)** (3, 4)

(b)

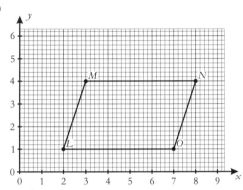

(c) parallelogram

S60 **(a)** **(i)** (3, 2) **(ii)** (8, 5)

(b)

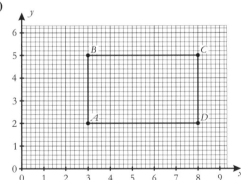

(c) 15 cm²

S61 **(a)** (3.5, 1) **(b)** (1, 2)

S62 4.8 cm

S63 **(a)** 4.5 m **(b)** 150°

S64

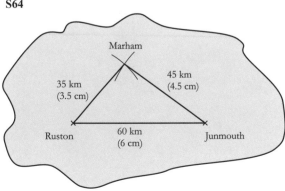

S65 **(a)** 70 km

(b) 135°

(c)

S66 **(a)** 600 m

(b)

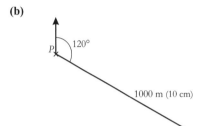

S67 **(a)** Reflection in the x-axis

(b) Translation of 5 units to the left

S68 **(a)** Rotation of 180° about (2, 0)

(b)

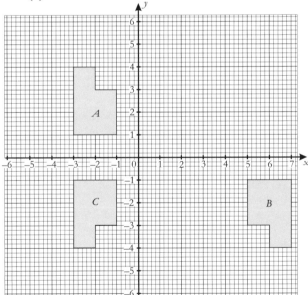

(c) Reflection in the line $x = 2$

Answers

S69 **(a)**

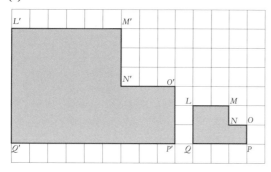

(b) No, they are the same shape but not the same size. The shapes are similar but not congruent.

S70

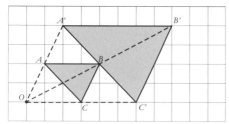

S71 400 m ÷ 50 s = 8 m/s

S72 182 miles ÷ 3.5 h = 52 mph

S73 62 km/h × 1.5 h = 93 km

S74 5004 kg ÷ 1.2 m³ = 4170 kg/m³

S75 **(a)** 25 000 kg

(b) 25 000 kg ÷ 200 kg/m³ = 125 m³

H1 **(a)** **(i)** 14 mm   **(ii)** 87 mm

(b) The beef tomatoes are generally larger in diameter than the plum tomatoes, and are a more consistent size.

H2 **(a)** **(i)** 10 g   **(ii)** 60 g

(b) Although the means are the same, the weights of the South African Green apples vary more.

H3 **(a)** 78 kg   **(b)** 74 kg

(c) The mode is not a good indicator. It is the lowest weight.

H4 **(a)** £546.63   **(b)** £56

(c) The mean does not give a good indication, it is distorted by an extreme value (£4002).

H5 **(a)**

	Balcony	No Balcony	Totals
Men	18	27	45
Women	21	26	47
Children	37	48	85
Totals	76	101	177

(b) 21 women

H6 **(a)**

	$h \leqslant 5$ ft	5 ft $< h < 6$ ft	$h \geqslant 6$ ft	Totals
Men	3	8	5	16
Women	5	9	2	16
Totals	8	17	7	32

(b) 5

H7 **(a)** 1 egg   **(b)** 1.5 eggs   **(c)** 1.72 eggs

H8 **(a)** 1.35 goals   **(b)** 1 goal

H9 **(a)** $20 < t \leqslant 40$

(b) Class $40 < t \leqslant 60$ because the median is the 25th value, which is in this class.

(c) 46 seconds

H10 **(a)** Wednesday   **(b)** 17 hours

H11 **(a)**

Type of Pet	Dog	Cat	Bird	No Pet
Frequency	7	6	3	6

(b)

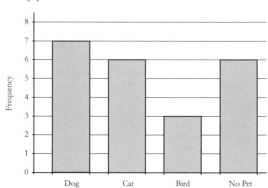

H12 **(a)** **(i)** 30   **(ii)** 25

(b)

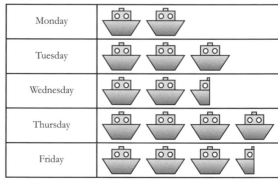

represents 10 barges

110

H13 (a) 6

(b)

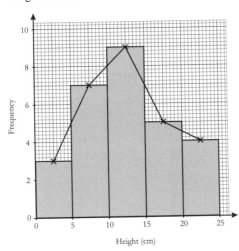

Number	
Algebra	
Shape, Space & Measures	
Handling Data	

represents 2 people

(c) 22

H14 (a) $10 < h \leqslant 15$

(b) This question can be answered by drawing a histogram or a frequency polygon. Both possible answers are shown on the same diagram below.

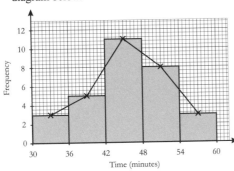

H15 (a)

Time (T mins)	Tally	Frequency
$30 \leqslant T < 36$	|||	3
$36 \leqslant T < 42$	|||||	5
$42 \leqslant T < 48$	||||| |||||		11
$48 \leqslant T < 54$	||||| |||	8
$54 \leqslant T < 60$	|||	3

(b) This question can be answered by drawing a histogram or a frequency polygon. Both possible answers are shown on the same diagram below.

H16 (a)

1	3	4						
2	0	3	4	6	6	9		
3	0	1	3	4	6	8		
4	2	2	2	6	8	9		

(b) 42   **(c)** 32

H17 (a)

6	4	4	5	7	8	8	9		
7	0	0	1	1	2	2	2	2	3
8	1	3	7	7	9				
9	0	1	5						

(b) 72

H18 (a) 30°   **(b)** $\frac{1}{12}$

(c) 75   **(d)** 350

H19 (a)

Number of books	Angle of Sector
0 to 2	72°
3 to 5	192°
6 to 8	66°
9 or more	30°
	360°

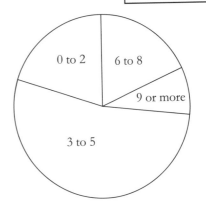

(b) $\frac{8}{15}$

H20 (a)

Colour	White	Red	Blue	Grey	
Number	88	22	18	52	Total
Angle	176°	44°	36°	104°	360°

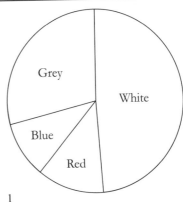

(b) $\frac{1}{10}$

Answers

HANDLING DATA

H21 **(a)** 23 March   **(b)** 30 March

     (c) Temperatures may not continue to fall.

H22 **(a)**

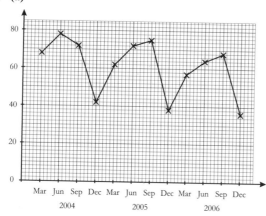

     (b) June 2004   **(c)** December 2006

H23 **(a)** & **(c)**

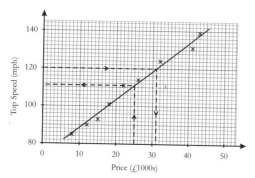

     (b) Strong positive correlation

     (d) **(i)** £31 000

          (ii) 111 mph

H24 **(a)** & **(c)**

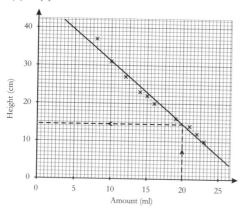

     (b) The height of the plants decreases as the
amount of Thunder Growth Feed they are given
increases (strong negative correlation).

     (d) 14.5 cm

H25 There isn't any correlation between the height above
ground and the leaf size.

H26 $\frac{1}{2}$ or 0.5

H27 **(a)** $\frac{1}{6}$ **(b)** $\frac{1}{3}$

H28 **(a)** **(i)** White

          (ii) There are more white spaces.

     (b)

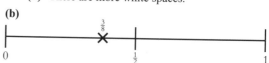

H29 **(a)** $\frac{7}{15}$ **(b)** $\frac{8}{15}$

H30 **(a)** $\frac{1}{4}$ **(b)** $\frac{3}{4}$

H31 **(a)** 40   **(b)** 120

H32 **(a)** 20   **(b)** 10

H33 **(a)** 0.2   **(b)** 72

H34 **(a)**

		DICE					
	+	1	2	3	4	5	6
C O I N	2	3	4	5	6	7	8
	3	4	5	6	7	8	9

     (b) **(i)** $\frac{1}{6}$ **(ii)** $\frac{5}{12}$ **(iii)** 0

H35 **(a)**

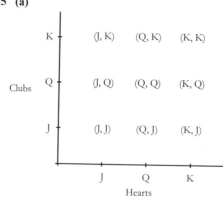

     (b) 9   **(c)** $\frac{1}{9}$

H36 **(a)** People may prefer to remain anonymous.

     (b) The question is leading, as it encourages you to
say 'yes'. Questions should never start 'Do you
agree...'.

     (c) The choices should be numbers. 'Occasionally', for
example, may mean once a month to one person
and once a week to another.